QUESTIONS AND ANSWE
'A' LEVEL PURE AND
APPLIED MATHEMATICS

Questions & Answers

PURE & APPLIED 'A' LEVEL MATHEMATICS

R. H. Evans
B.A., B.Sc.

Checkmate / Arnold

First Edition Published December 1983.
Second Edition Published 1986
by Checkmate Publications,
4 Ainsdale Close, Bromborough, Wirral L63 0EU.
This Edition Published in association with

Edward Arnold (Publishers) Ltd.,
41 Bedford Square, London WC1B 3DQ

Edward Arnold (Australia) Pty Ltd.,
80 Waverley Road, Caulfield East,
Victoria 3145, Australia

Edward Arnold, 3 East Read Street,
Baltimore, Maryland 21202, U.S.A.

Printed and Bound by
Richard Clay (Chaucer Press), Bungay, Suffolk

ISBN 0 946973 35 0

INTRODUCTION

This book is intended to help students about to take examinations at G.C.E. A level in Pure and Applied Mathematics. Although the questions set in this text are from University of London papers, students taking examinations of other boards such as AEB and JMB may also find them of use. The Board has given its kind permission for reproduction of their questions in this text, however we must point out that this in no way implies that the solutions given are the responsibility of the Board. The solutions are the sole responsibility of the author.

The format of the book is specifically structured so that students may read and attempt questions before referring to the suggested answer. In this respect it is a useful self testing program.

The author of this text is a long standing member of the teaching profession specialising in Mathematics and Statistics. Prior to entering the profession many years ago he was an engineer and thus his experience in the applied field is invaluable.

PAPER 2 (PURE MATHEMATICS)

Page

1. The function f is defined by 1

$$f : x \to \frac{x+3}{x-1}, \quad x \in \mathbb{R}, \quad x \neq 1.$$

Find

(a) the range of f,

(b) ff(x),

(c) $f^{-1}(x)$. (6 marks)

---

2. When the polynomial P(x), where 1

$$P(x) \equiv ax^3 + 5x^2 + 2x + b,$$

is divided by (x - 1) the remainder is 2. When P(x) is divided by (x - 2) the remainder is 5. Determine the constants a and b.

(6 marks)

---

3. Find the set of values of x for which 2

$$|x - 1| - |2x + 1| > 0.$$

(5 marks)

---

4. Prove that $\sum_{r=1}^{n} r(r+1) = 1/3n(n+1)(n+2)$. 2

Evaluate $\sum_{r=1}^{20} r(r-1)$.

(5 marks)

---

5. Given that $y = \frac{3x+k}{x^2-1}$, where x is real and k is a constant, 3

show that y can take all real values if $|k| < 3$.

(6 marks)

Page

6. Find the number of different permutations of the 8 letters of the word SYLLABUS. 3

Find the number of different selections of 5 letters which can be made from the letters of the word SYLLABUS.

(6 marks)

---

7. Given that 4

$$3 \sin x - \cos x \equiv R \sin (x - \alpha),$$

where $R > 0$ and $0^0 < \alpha < 90^0$, find the values of R and α correct to one decimal place.

Hence find one value of x between 0^0 and 360^0 for which the curve $y = 3 \sin x - \cos x$ has a turning point.

(6 marks)

---

8. Find y in terms of x given that 4

$$x \frac{dy}{dx} = y(y + 1)$$

and $y = 4$ when $x = 2$.

(7 marks)

---

9. The point A has position vector $\mathbf{i} + 4\mathbf{j} - 3\mathbf{k}$ referred to the origin O. The line L has vector equation $\mathbf{r} = t\,\mathbf{i}$. The plane π contains the line L and the point A. Find 5

(a) a vector which is normal to the plane π,

(b) a vector equation for the plane π,

(c) the cosine of the acute angle between OA and the line L.

(7 marks)

Page

10. Page 6

v	5	10	15	20	25
R	149	175	219	280	359

The table shows corresponding values of variables R and v obtained in an experiment. By drawing a suitable linear graph, show that these pairs of values may be regarded as approximations to values satisfying a relation of the form $R = a + bv^2$, where a and b are constants.

Use your graph to estimate the values of a and b, giving your answers to 2 significant figures.

(8 marks)

---

11. Given that $y = \frac{x^2 - 1}{2x^2 + 1}$, find $\frac{dy}{dx}$ and state the set of values of x for which $\frac{dy}{dx}$ is positive. Page 7

Find the greatest and least values of y for $0 < x < 1$.

(7 marks)

---

12. Find (a) $\int x \ln x \, dx$, (b) $\int \frac{x}{\sqrt{(x - 2)}} dx$. Page 7

(8 marks)

---

13. Given that $z = \sqrt{3} + i$, find the modulus and argument of (a) z^2, (b) $\frac{1}{z}$. Page 8

Show in an Argand diagram the points representing the complex numbers z, z^2 and $\frac{1}{z}$.

(8 marks)

---

14. Show graphically, or otherwise, that the equation $\ln x = 4 - x$ has only one real root and prove that this root lies between 2.9 and 3. Page 8

Continued....

14. (Continued) — Page

By taking 2.9 as a first approximation to this root and applying the Newton-Raphson process once to the equation $\ln x - 4 + x = 0$, or otherwise, find a second approximation, giving your answer to 3 significant figures. — 8

(8 marks)

---

15. Given that $E(x) \equiv \dfrac{15x - 6}{(1 - 2x)(2 - x)}$ — 9

express E(x) in partial fractions.

Hence, or otherwise, for $|x| < 1/2$, express E(x) in the form of a series of terms in ascending powers of x up to and including the term in x^2.

(9 marks)

---

16. Sketch the curve given parametrically by — 9

$$x = t^2, \quad y = t^3.$$

Show that an equation of the normal to the curve at the point A(4,8) is $x + 3y - 28 = 0$.

This normal meets the x-axis at the point N. Find the area of the region enclosed by the arc OA of the curve, the line segment AN and the x-axis.

(12 marks)

---

17. A student must answer exactly 7 out of 10 questions in an examination. Given that she must answer <u>at least</u> 3 of the first 5 questions, determine the number of ways in which she may select the 7 questions. — 10

(4 marks)

---

18. Find the set of values of x for which — 10

$$x > |3x - 8|.$$

(5 marks)

Page

19. Show that the area of the finite region enclosed by the line $y = 4x$ and the curve $y^2 = 16x$ is 2/3. — 11

(4 marks)

---

20. Express $\sin x - \cos x$ in the form $R \sin(x - \alpha)$, where R is positive and α is an acute angle. Hence, or otherwise, find, in radians, the general solution of the equation — 12

$$\sin x - \cos x = 1.$$

(6 marks)

---

21. The series $\sum_{r=1}^{n+1} U_r$ is a geometric series with common ratio k, where $k^2 \neq 1$. Show that the series $\sum_{r=1}^{n} (u_r u_{r+1})$ is a geometric series and that its sum is equal to — 12

$$\frac{u_1^2\, k(1 - k^{2n})}{(1 - k^2)}$$

(6 marks)

---

22. Given that $f(x) \equiv x^2 - 6x + 10$, show that $f(x) > 0$ for all real values of x. — 13

Using the same axes sketch the graphs of $y = f(x)$ and $y = 1/f(x)$.

(6 marks)

---

23. Given that — 13

$$f(x) \equiv \frac{1}{(x + 1)(x + 3)},$$

express $f(x)$ in partial fractions and find

$$\sum_{r=1}^{n} \frac{1}{(2r + 1)(2r + 3)}$$

(7 marks)

Page

24. A cylindrical vessel, closed at both ends, is made of thin material and contains a volume $16\pi \text{ m}^3$. Given that the total exterior surface area of the vessel is a minimum, find its height and base radius. 14

(7 marks)

---

25. The function g is defined by 14

$$g:x \to \frac{2x + 5}{x - 3}, \quad x \in R, x \neq 3.$$

Sketch the graph of the function g. Find an expression for $g^{-1}(x)$, specifying its domain.

(7 marks)

---

26. The two lines with vector equations 15

$$\mathbf{r} = \mathbf{k} + s(\mathbf{i} + \mathbf{j}) \text{ and } \mathbf{r} = \mathbf{k} + t(-\mathbf{i} + \mathbf{k})$$

intersect at the point A. Write down the position vector of A.

Find a vector perpendicular to both of the lines and hence, or otherwise, obtain a vector equation of the plane containing the two lines.

(8 marks)

---

27. By considering the roots of the equation $f'(x) = 0$, or otherwise, prove that the equation $f(x) = 0$, where $f(x) \equiv x^3 + 2x + 4$, has only one real root. Show that this root lies in the interval $-2 < x < -1$. 15

Use the iterative procedure

$$x_{n+1} = -\frac{1}{6}(x_n^3 - 4x_n + 4), \; x_1 = -1,$$

to find two further approximations to the root of the equation, giving your final answer to 2 decimal places.

(8 marks)

	Page
28. Determine the value of the constant k given that in the expansion of $$\frac{1 - kx^2}{(1 - x^2)^{1/2}}$$ in ascending powers of x for $|x| < 1$, the coefficient of x^2 is zero. Using this value of k, find the first three non-zero terms of the expansion. (9 marks)	16
29. Solve the differential equation $$\frac{dy}{dx} = \frac{(y^2 - 1)}{x},$$ where $y = 2$ when $x = 1$, giving y in terms of x. (10 marks)	16
30. Find the modulus and argument of each of the complex numbers z_1 and z_2, where $$z_1 = \frac{1 + i}{1 - i}, \quad z_2 = \frac{\sqrt{2}}{1 - i}$$ Plot the points representing z_1, z_2 and $z_1 + z_2$ on an Argand diagram. Deduce from your diagram that $$\tan(3\pi/8) = 1 + \sqrt{2}.$$ (12 marks)	17
31. A curve is defined with parameter t by the equations $$x = at^2, \quad y = 2at$$ The tangent and normal at the point P with parameter t_1 cut	17

Continued....

31. (Continued) **Page**

the x-axis at T and N respectively. Prove that

$$PT/PN = | t_1 |.$$

(12 marks)

---

32. Find, in each case, the set of values of x for which **18**

(a) $$\frac{1}{3 - x} < \frac{1}{x - 2}$$

(b) $$| 3 + 2x | < | 4 - x |.$$

(8 marks)

PAPER 3 (APPLIED MATHEMATICS)

33. Prove, by integration, that the distance of the centre of mass of a uniform solid right circular cone, of height h, from its plane base is h/4. **19**

The cone is freely hinged at its vertex and is kept in equilibrium by a light rigid rod of length h joining the centre of the base to a point $h\sqrt{3}$ directly above the vertex. Show that the tension in the rod is $W\sqrt{3}/4$, where W is the weight of the cone.

Find the magnitude of the reaction at the hinge.

---

34. Prove that the elastic energy of a light spring of natural length a and modulus of elasticity λ, stretched by an amount x, is $\lambda x^2/(2a)$. **20**

A trolley of mass m runs down a smooth track of constant inclination $\pi/6$ to the horizontal, carrying at its front a light spring of natural length a and modulus mga/c, where c is constant. When the spring is fully compressed it is of length a/4, and it obeys Hooke's law up to this point. After the trolley has travelled a distance b from

Continued....

34. (Continued) | Page

rest the spring meets a fixed stop. Show that, when the spring has been compressed a distance x, where $x < 3a/4$, the speed v of the trolley is given by | 20

$$cv^2/g = c(b + x) - x.$$

Given that $c = a/10$ and $b = 2a$, find the total distance covered by the trolley before it momentarily comes to rest for the first time.

---

35. A particle moving on a straight line with speed v experiences a retardation of magnitude $be^{v/u}$, where b and u are constants. Given that the particle is travelling with speed u at time $t = 0$, show that the time t_1 for the speed to decrease to 1/2 u is given by | 21

$$bt_1 = u(e^{-1/2} - e^{-1}).$$

Find the further time t_2 for the particle to come to rest.

Deduce that $t_2/t_1 = e^{1/2}$.

Find, in terms of b and u, an expression for the distance travelled in decelerating from speed u to rest.

---

36. At time t two points P and Q have position vectors p and q respectively, where | 22

$$p = 2a\mathbf{i} + (a \cos wt)\mathbf{j} + (a \sin wt)\mathbf{k}$$

$$q = (a \sin wt)\mathbf{i} - (a \cos wt)\mathbf{j} + 3a\mathbf{k}$$

and a, w are constants. Find r, the position vector of P relative to Q, and v, the velocity of P relative to Q. Find also the values of t for which r and v are perpendicular.

Determine the smallest and greatest distances between P and Q.

Page

37. An artificial satellite of mass m moves under the action of a gravitational force which is directed towards the centre, O, of the earth and is of magnitude F. The orbit of the satellite is a circle of radius a and centre O. Obtain an expression for T, the period of the satellite, in terms of m, a and F. 23

Show that, if the gravitational force acting on a body of mass m at a distance r from O is $m\mu/r^2$, where μ is a constant, then $T^2\mu = 4\pi^2 a^3$.

Assuming that the radius of the earth is 6400 km and that the acceleration due to gravity at the surface of the earth is 10 m s^{-2}, show that $\mu = (6.4)^2\, 10^{13}$ $m^3 s^{-2}$.

Hence, or otherwise, find the period of revolution, in hours to 2 decimal places, of the satellite when it travels in a circular orbit 600 km above the surface of the earth.

---

38. A particle A, of mass m, is moving on a smooth horizontal plane with speed v when it strikes directly a particle B, of mass 3m, which is at rest on the plane. The coefficient of restitution between A and B is 1/2 and after impact B moves with speed 3u. Find, in terms of u, the value of v and the speed of A after impact. Find also, in terms of m and u, 24

(a) the magnitude of the impulse of the blow received by B,
(b) the kinetic energy lost in the impact.

A third particle, C, of mass 6m, is at rest on the plane and is connected by an elastic spring, of natural length l and modulus of elasticity kmg, to a point D on the plane so that BCD is a straight line and CD = l. Particle B strikes C and is brought to rest by the impact. Particle C then moves a distance 1/4 l before coming momentarily to rest. Show that

$$k = \frac{216u^2}{gl}$$

Page

39. A particle is projected with speed u at an angle of elevation α to the horizontal. Given that R is the range attained on a horizontal plane through the point of projection, and h is the maximum height of the trajectory, prove that — 25

$$R = 2c \sin \alpha \cos \alpha,$$

$$2h = c \sin^2 \alpha,$$

where $c = u^2/g$.

Hence prove that $R^2 = c^2 - (c - 4h)^2$.

If u is held fixed while α varies, so that R and h vary, deduce from the last equation that R is an increasing function of h when $h < c/4$. Hence, prove that, if a particle is projected with speed 30 m s^{-1} from the floor of a horizontal tunnel of height 20 m, the greatest range which can be attained in the tunnel is about 89.4 m.

[Take g as 10 m s^{-2}.]

---

40. (i) The events A and B are such that — 26

$$P(A) = 0.4, P(B) = 0.45, P(A \quad B) = 0.68.$$

Show that the events A and B are neither mutually exclusive nor independent.

(ii) A bag contains 12 red balls, 8 blue balls and 4 white balls. Three balls are taken from the bag at random and without replacement. Find the probability that all three balls are of the same colour.

Find also the probability that all three balls are of different colours.

---

41. Show by integration that the centre of mass of a uniform triangular lamina PQR is at a distance 1/3 h from QR, where hs is the length of the altitude PS. — 27

Continued....

41. (Continued) **Page**

A uniform piece of cardboard is in the form of a rectangle ABCD, in which AB = 10a, BC = 6a, and E is the point in AB such that AE = 4a. The cardboard is folded along CE so that the edge CB lies along the edge CD to form a trapezium shaped lamina AECD and the triangular part CEB is of double thickness. Find the distance of the centre of mass of the lamina AECD from (a) AD, (b) AE. Show that, when this lamina is freely suspended from the vertex A, the edge AD makes an angle $\tan^{-1}(11/9)$ with the vertical. 27

The lamina AECD, which is of weight W, is next suspended by two vertical strings attached at A and D and is at rest with AD horizontal. Find the tension in each string.

---

42. A uniform rod AB, of length 2l and weight W, is in equilibrium with the end A on a rough horizontal floor and the end B against a smooth vertical wall. The rod makes an angle $\tan^{-1} 2$ with the horizontal and is in a vertical plane which is perpendicular to the wall. Find the least possible value of μ , the coefficient of friction between the floor and the rod. 29

Given that $\mu = 5/16$, find the distance from A of the highest point of the rod at which a particle of weight W can be attached without disturbing equilibrium.

---

43. (i) The brakes of a train, which is travelling at 108 km h^{-1} , are applied as the train passes point A. The brakes produce a constant retardation of magnitude 3f m s^{-2} until the speed of the train is reduced to 36 km h^{-1}. The train travels at this speed for a distance and is then uniformly accelerated at f m s^{-2} until it again reaches a speed of 108 km h^{-1} as it passes point B. The time taken by the train in travelling from A to B, a distance of 4 km, is 4 minutes. Sketch the speed/time graph for this motion and hence calculate 30

(a) the value of f,
(b) the distance travelled at 36 km h^{-1}.

Continued....

43. (Continued) Page

(ii) A particle moves in a straight line with variable acceleration $\frac{k}{1+v}$ m s^{-2}, where k is a constant and v m s^{-1} is the speed of the particle when it has travelled a distance x m. Find the distance moved by the particle as its speed increases from 0 to u m s^{-1}. 30

---

44. At time t = 0 a ship A is at the point L and a ship B is at the point with position vector $10\mathbf{j}$ nautical miles referred to O. The velocities of the two ships are constant. Ship A sails at 17 knots, where 1 knot is 1 nautical mile per hour, in the direction of the vector $8\mathbf{i} + 15\mathbf{j}$ and ship B sails at 15 knots in the direction of the vector $3\mathbf{i} + 4\mathbf{j}$ Write down 32

(a) the velocity vector of each ship,
(b) the velocity of B relative to A,
(c) the position vector of B relative to A at time t hours.

Given that visibility is 5 nautical miles, show that the ships are within sight of each other for $\sqrt{6}$ hours.

---

45. (Throughout this question take g as 10 m s^{-2}.) 33

(i) A ball is kicked from a point A on level ground and hits a goalpost at a point 4 m above the ground. The goalpost is at a distance of 32 m from A. Initially the velocity of the ball makes an angle $\tan^{-1} 3/4$ with the ground. Show that the initial speed of the ball is 20 m s^{-1}. Find the speed of the ball when it hits the goalpost.

(ii) A particle is attached to one end of a light string, the other end of which is fixed. When the particle moves in a horizontal circle with speed 2 m s^{-1}, the string makes an angle $\tan^{-1} (5/12)$ with the vertical. Show that the length of the string is approximately 2.5 m.

Page

46\. A particle of mass 2m is on a plane inclined at an angle $\tan^{-1} 3/4$ to the horizontal. The particle is attached to one end of a light inextensible string. This string runs parallel to a line of greatest slope of the plane, passes over a small smooth pulley at the top of the plane and then hangs vertically carrying a particle of mass 3m at its other end. The system is released from rest with the string taut. Find the acceleration of each particle and the tension in the string when the particles are moving freely, given that — 34

(a) the plane is smooth,

(b) the plane is rough and the coefficient of friction between the particle and the plane is 1/4.

47\. (i) A sphere of mass 3m is moving with speed 2u when it collides directly with another sphere, of the same radius but of mass m, which is moving in the opposite direction with speed u. The coefficient of restitution between the spheres is 1/3. Calculate — 35

(a) the speed of each sphere immediately after impact,
(b) the magnitude of the impulse received by each sphere on impact.

(ii) A pump, working at an effective rate of 41 kW, raises 80 kg of water per second from a depth of 20 m. Calculate the speed with which the water is delivered.

(Take g as 10 m s^{-2}.)

48\. (i) Events A and B are independent. The probability of A occurring is 1/3 and the probability of B occurring is 1/4. Find the probability of — 36

(a) neither event occurring,
(b) one and only one of the two events occurring.

Continued....

48. (Continued) Page

(ii) A bag contains 10 balls, of which 3 are red, 3 are blue and 4 are white. Three balls are to be drawn one at a time, at random and without replacement, from the bag. 36

Find the probability that

- (a) the first 2 balls drawn will be of different colours,
- (b) all 3 balls drawn will be of the same colour,
- (c) exactly 2 of the balls drawn will be of the same colour.

---

49. (i) State the centre and radius of the circle which has vector equation 37

$$\mathbf{r} = 6\mathbf{i} + 3\mathbf{j} + 6(\mathbf{i}\cos\theta + \mathbf{j}\sin\theta).$$

A particle P, of mass 2 kg, moves on this circle with constant angular speed $\pi/12$ radians per second. Write down the position vector of P at time t given that, at $t = 0$, P is at the point corresponding to $\theta = 0$.

(ii) A particle, moving on the smooth inside surface of a fixed spherical bowl of radius 2 m, describes a horizontal circle at a distance 8/5 m below the centre of the bowl. Prove that the speed of the particle is 3 m/s.

(Take g as 10 m/s^2)

---

50. The maximum rate of working of the engine of a car is SkW. Against a constant resistance, the car can attain a maximum speed of u m/s on level ground and a maximum speed of 1/2u m/s directly up a slope of inclination α, where $\sin\alpha = \frac{1}{16}$. Calculate the maximum speed of the car up a slope of inclination β, where $\sin\beta = 1/8$, assuming that the resistance remains unchanged. 38

Continued....

50. (Continued) Page

Given that $S = 15$ and that $u = 20$, find the maximum acceleration that can be attained when the car is towing a trailer of mass 300 kg at 10 m/s on level ground. It may be assumed that the resistance to the motion of the car remains unchanged and that the resistance to the motion of the trailer can be neglected. 38

(Take g as 10 m/s^2.)

---

1. $f : x \longmapsto \frac{x+3}{x-1}, \quad x \in \mathbb{R}, \ x \neq 1$

(a) as $x \to -\infty$, $f(x) \to 1$

as $x \to +\infty$, $f(x) \to 1$

as $x \to 1$ (from below), $f(x) \to -\infty$

as $x \to 1$ (from above), $f(x) \to +\infty$

$\therefore$ Range of f is $\mathbb{R}$, $f(x) \neq 1$

(b) $ff(x) : x \longmapsto \left\{ \frac{\frac{x+3}{x-1} + 3}{\frac{x+3}{x-1} - 1} \right\}$

i.e., $x \longmapsto x, \quad x \in \mathbb{R}, \ x \neq 1$

(c) $f^{-1}(x) : x \longmapsto \frac{3x+1}{1-x}, \quad x \in \mathbb{R}, \ x \neq 1$

---

2. $P(x) \equiv ax^3 + 5x^2 + 2x + b$

By Remainder Theorem, $P(1) = 2$ and $P(2) = 5$

$\therefore \quad a + 5 + 2 + b = 2$ ------ ①

$8a + 20 + 4 + b = 5$ ------ ②

② − ① $\therefore$ $7a + 15 + 2 = 3$

$\therefore \quad 7a = -14$

$\therefore \quad a = -2$

subs $a = -2$ in (1) $\therefore$ $-2 + 5 + 2 + b = 2$

$\therefore \quad b = -3$

June 84 – B2 – 6 and 5

3 We require $|x-1| - |2x+1| > 0$

ie, $|x-1| > |2x+1|$

ie, $(x-1)^2 > (2x+1)^2$

ie, $x^2-2x+1 > 4x^2+4x+1$

ie, $0 > 3x^2+6x$

ie, $0 > (x+2)x$

True for $\{x > -2,\ x < 0\}$

and $\{x < -2,\ x > 0\}$, impossible

thus $|x-1| - |2x+1| > 0$

for $-2 < x < 0$

---

4 We are required to prove $\sum_{r=1}^{n} r(r+1) = \frac{1}{3}n(n+1)(n+2)$

This can be done by "induction" but is not required by the question.

$$\sum_{r=1}^{n} r(r+1) = \sum_{r=1}^{n} r^2 + \sum_{r=1}^{n} r = \frac{n}{6}(n+1)(2n+1) + \frac{n}{2}(n+1)$$

$$= \frac{n(n+1)(2n+1+3)}{6}$$

$$= \frac{n(n+1)(n+2)}{3} \quad \text{as required}$$

$$\sum_{r=1}^{n} r(r-1) = \sum_{r=1}^{n} r^2 - \sum_{r=1}^{n} r = \frac{n}{6}(n+1)(2n+1-3)$$

$$= \frac{n}{3}(n+1)(n-1)$$

$$\therefore \sum_{r=1}^{20} = \frac{20}{3}(21)(19)$$

$$= 2660$$

---

5. $y = \dfrac{3x + k}{x^2+1}$

$\therefore\ yx^2 - y = 3x + k$

$\therefore\ yx^2 - 3x - (k+y) = 0$

for x real, "$b^2 \geqslant 4ac$" (with usual notation)

ie $9 \geqslant -4y(k+y)$

ie $4y^2 + 4ky + 9 \geqslant 0$

ie $(2y+k)^2 + 9 - k^2 \geqslant 0$ (by "completing the square")

Now $(2y+k)^2 \geqslant 0$ for all real y and k

$\therefore$ we require $9 - k^2 \geqslant 0$

ie $9 \geqslant k^2$

ie $3 \geqslant |k|$

<u>This requirement is satisfied if $|k| < 3$</u>

6

SYLLABUS If each letter were different, there would be 8! permutations. The two S's and two L's can each be arranged in 2! ways without affecting order. Thus, the number of permatations when this is taken into consideration

$$= \frac{8!}{2!2!} = \underline{10080}$$

For selections (combinations) of 5 letters we can have:-

L's	S's	Others	No of combinations
0	0	5	0
0	1	4	$4C4 = 1$
0	2	3	$4C3 = 4$
1	0	4	$4C4 = 1$
1	1	3	$4C3 = 4$
1	2	2	$4C2 = 6$
2	0	3	$4C3 = 4$
2	1	2	$4C2 = 6$
2	2	1	$4C1 = 4$

Total <u>30 Selections</u>

7.

$3\sin x - \cos x \equiv R\sin(x-\alpha)$

ie, $3\sin x - \cos x \equiv R\sin x\cos\alpha - R\cos x\sin\alpha$

$\therefore \quad R\cos\alpha = 3$

$R\sin\alpha = 1$

$R^2 = 1^2 + 3^2$

$R = \sqrt{1+9} = 3.16$

$= \underline{3.2}$ to 2 d.p

R

$R\sin\alpha = 1$

α

$R\cos\alpha = 3$

$\tan\alpha = \frac{1}{3} \quad \therefore \underline{\alpha = 18.4°}$

let $y = 3\sin x - \cos x$

ie $y = 3.2\sin(x - 18.4°)$

There is a turning point when $\sin(x - 18.4°) = 1$

ie $x - 18.4° = 90°$

$\therefore \quad \underline{x = 108.4°}$

8

$$x\frac{dy}{dx} = y(y+1)$$

$$\therefore \int \frac{dy}{y(y+1)} = \int \frac{dx}{x}$$

$$\therefore \int\left(\frac{1}{y} - \frac{1}{y+1}\right)dy = \int \frac{dx}{x}$$

$$\ln y - \ln(y+1) = \ln x + A \qquad (A \text{ is a constant})$$

$$\ln \frac{y}{y+1} = \ln x + A$$

$y = 4,\ x = 2 \quad \therefore \ln\frac{4}{5} = \ln 2 + A$

$$\therefore A = \ln\frac{2}{5}$$

$$\therefore \ln\left(\frac{y}{y+1}\right) = \ln x + \ln\frac{2}{5}$$

$$\therefore \frac{y}{y+1} = \frac{2}{5}x$$

$$\therefore 5y = 2xy + 2x$$

$$\therefore \underline{y = \frac{2x}{5-2x}}$$

9 The plane π contains the point A, with position vector $= (\bar{i} + 4\bar{j} - 3\bar{k})$ and the line L, with equation $\bar{r} = t\bar{i}$

Let B be the point on L for which $t = 1$.

$\therefore$ B has position vector $= \bar{i}$. (Note - L passes through origin)

Referring to the diagram,

$\bar{AB} = \bar{i} - (\bar{i} + 4\bar{j} - 3\bar{k}) = -4\bar{j} + 3\bar{k}$

$\bar{r} = \bar{i}$

Suppose $(a\bar{i} + b\bar{j} + c\bar{k})$ is a vector normal to the plane (and therefore normal to $\bar{AB}$ and $\bar{r}$)

Using Scalar Products.

$(a\bar{i} + b\bar{j} + c\bar{k})\cdot(-4\bar{i} + 3\bar{k}) = 0$ and $(a\bar{i} + b\bar{j} + c\bar{k})\cdot t\bar{i}$

$\therefore -4b + 3c = 0$ $\qquad \therefore at = 0$

$\therefore 3c = 4b$ $\qquad \therefore a = 0$

$\therefore$ Vector normal to the plane $= (b\bar{j} + \frac{4b}{3}\bar{k})$

$= d(3\bar{j} + 4\bar{k})$

$(d = b/3)$

$\therefore$ Any scalar multiple of $(3\bar{j} + 4\bar{k})$ is normal to the plane

Equation of plane :- $\bar{r}\cdot(3\bar{j} + 4\bar{k}) = (\bar{i} + 4\bar{j} - 3\bar{k})\cdot(3\bar{j} + 4\bar{k})$

ie, $\bar{r}\cdot(3\bar{j} + 4\bar{k}) = 12 - 12$

ie, $\bar{r}\cdot(3\bar{j} + 4\bar{k}) = 0$

for $\bar{OA}$ and $\bar{r}$

Scalar product :- $(\bar{i} + 4\bar{j} - 3\bar{k})\cdot(i) = \pm\sqrt{1^2+4^2+3^2}\,\sqrt{1^2}\cos\theta$

where θ = angle between $\bar{OA}$ and $\bar{i}$

$\therefore 1 + 0 + 0 = \pm\sqrt{26}\cos\theta$

$\therefore$ cosine of acute angle between $\bar{OA}$ and L $= \frac{1}{\sqrt{26}}$

10

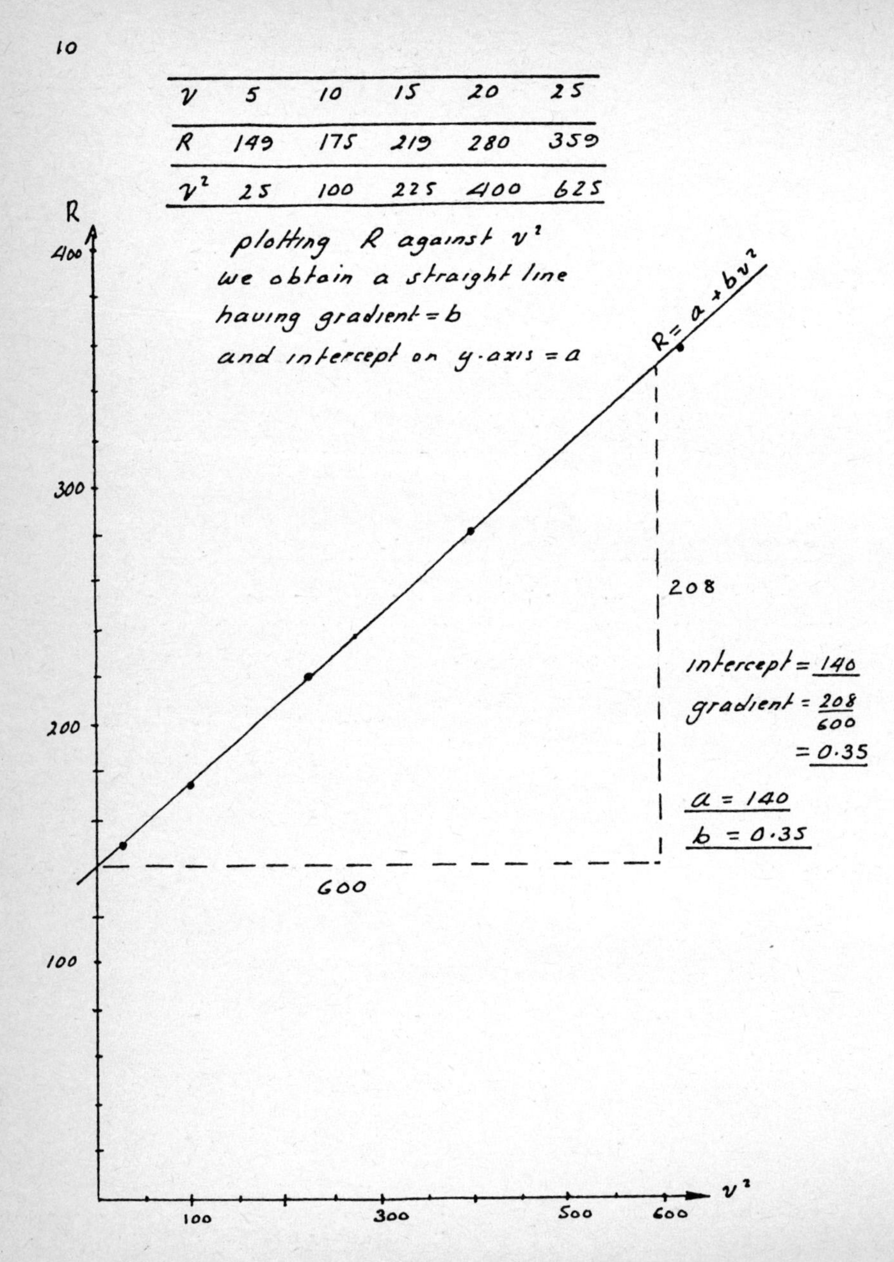

v	5	10	15	20	25
R	149	175	219	280	359
v^2	25	100	225	400	625

11. $y = \frac{x^2-1}{2x^2+1}$, $\frac{dy}{dx} = \frac{(2x^2+1)(2x) - (x^2-1)(4x)}{(2x^2+1)^2}$

$= \frac{4x^3+2x - 4x^3 + 4x}{(2x^2+1)^2}$

$= \frac{6x}{(2x^2+1)^2}$

$(2x^2+1)^2 > 0$ for all real x

thus $\frac{dy}{dx} > 0$ for $6x > 0$

ie $\frac{dy}{dx} > 0$ for all real x

Greatest value of y (for $0 \le x \le 1$)

$= \frac{1-1}{2+1} = 0$

Least value of y (for $0 \le x \le 1$)

$= \frac{0-1}{0+1} = -1$

12. (a) Let $I = \int x \ln x \, dx$

By parts:– let $u = \ln x$ $\quad v = \int x \, dx$

$du = \frac{dx}{x}$ $\quad v = \frac{x^2}{2}$

$I = uv - \int v du = \frac{x^2}{2} \ln x - \int \frac{x^2}{2x} dx$

$= \frac{x^2}{4}(2 \ln x - x^2) + A = \frac{x^2}{4}(\ln x^2 - x^2) + A$

(b) Let $I = \int \frac{x}{\sqrt{(x-2)}} dx$

let $z^2 = x - 2$

$\therefore 2z dz = dx$

$I = \int \frac{(z^2+2)}{z} . 2z \, dz$

$= 2\int (z^2+2) \, dz$

$= 2\left(\frac{z^3}{3} + 2z\right) + B$

$= 2z\left(\frac{z^2}{3} + 2\right) + B$

$= 2(x-2)^{1/2}\left(\frac{x-2}{3} + 2\right) + B$

$= \frac{2}{3}(x-2)^{1/2}(x+4) + B$

13. $z = \sqrt{3} + i$

$z^2 = 2(1 + \sqrt{3}i)$

<u>modulus</u> of $z^2 = 2\sqrt{(1+3)} = 2\sqrt{4} = \underline{4}$.

<u>argument</u> of $z^2 = \tan^{-1}\sqrt{3} = \underline{\frac{\pi}{3}}$

$\frac{1}{z} = \frac{1}{\sqrt{3}+i} = \frac{\sqrt{3}-i}{4} = \frac{1}{4}(\sqrt{3}-i)$

<u>modulus</u> of $\frac{1}{z} = \frac{1}{4}\sqrt{(3+1)} = \underline{\frac{1}{2}}$

<u>argument</u> of $\frac{1}{z} = \tan^{-1}\frac{-1}{\sqrt{3}}$ (in 4th quadrant) $= \underline{-\frac{\pi}{6}}$

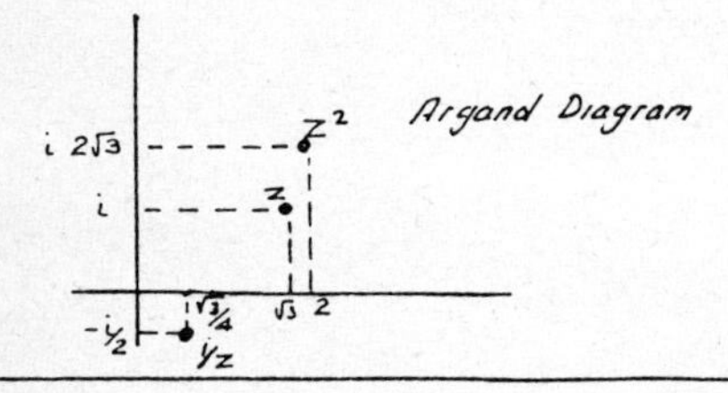

14.

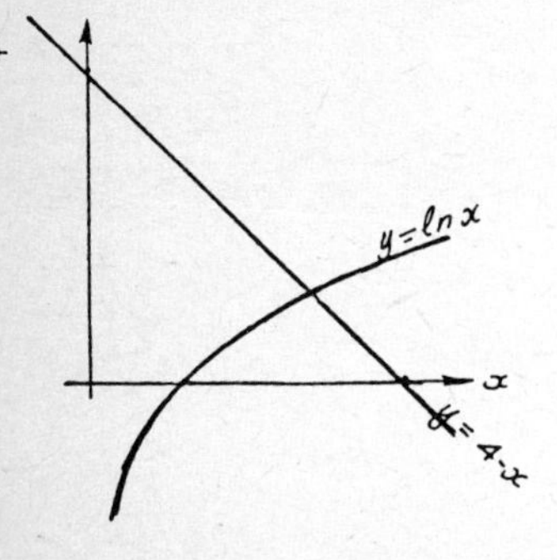

ln x is not defined for $x \leq 0$ and is a continuous increasing function for $x > 0$

$4 - x$ is a continuous decreasing function for all values of x

thus $\ln x = 4 - x$ has one, and only one, real root.

if $x = 2\cdot9$, $\ln x = 1\cdot065$ and $4 - x = 1\cdot1$ $\therefore \ln x < 4 - x$

if $x = 3\cdot0$, $\ln x = 1\cdot099$ and $4 - x = 1\cdot0$ $\therefore \ln x > 4 - x$

as $\ln x$ is increasing, $4-x$ decreasing $\ln x = 4 - x$ between $2\cdot9$ and 3.

Newton-Raphson, $x_1 = x_0 - \frac{f(x_0)}{f'(x_0)}$ $\quad f(x) = \ln x + x - 4$, $\quad f'(x) = 1/x + 1$

$$= 2\cdot9 - \frac{\ln 2\cdot9 + 2\cdot9 - 4}{\frac{1}{2\cdot9} + 1}$$

$$= 2\cdot926$$

$$= \underline{2\cdot93 \ (3 \text{ S.F})}$$

June 82 B2 13 and 14

15. $E(x) = \dfrac{15x-6}{(1-2x)(2-x)}$

By using partial fractions, we have:–

$$E(x) = \frac{1}{1-2x} - \frac{8}{2-x}$$

$$E(x) = (1-2x)^{-1} - 8(2-x)^{-1}$$

$$= \begin{cases} 1 + (-1)(-2x) + \dfrac{(-1)(-2)(-2x)^2}{2!} + \dots \\ -4\left(1 + (-1)(-\tfrac{x}{2}) + \dfrac{(-1)(-2)(-\tfrac{x}{2})^2}{2!} + \dots \right. \end{cases}$$

$$= \begin{cases} 1 + 2x + 4x^2 + \dots \\ -4 - 2x - x^2 + \dots \end{cases}$$

$\therefore$ up to, and including, term in x^2

we have $\underline{E(x) = -3 + 3x^2}$

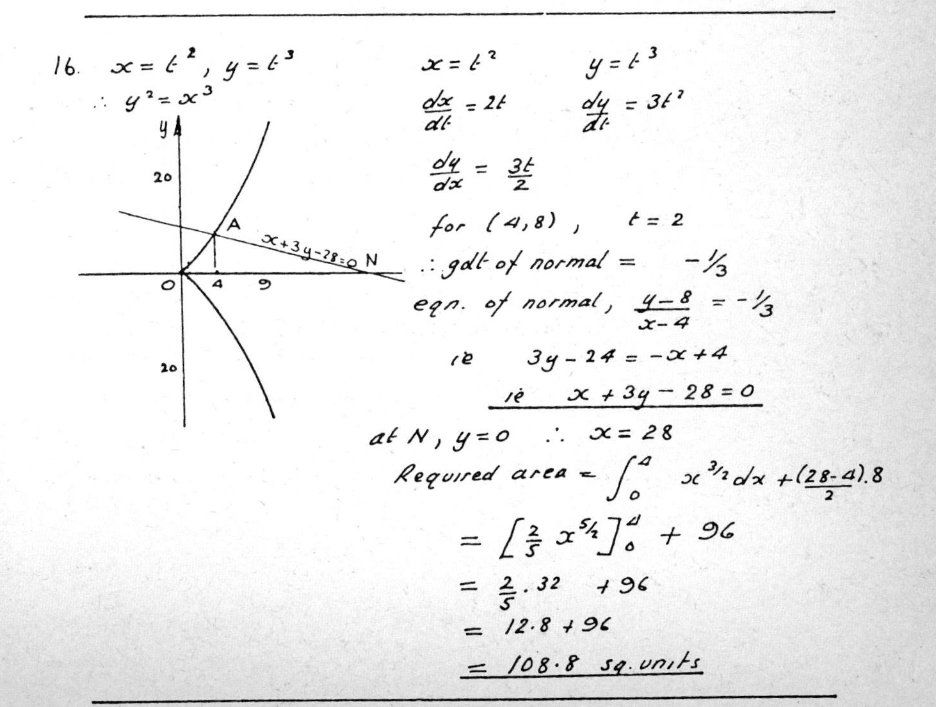

16. $x = t^2,\ y = t^3$

$\therefore y^2 = x^3$

$x = t^2$ $\qquad$ $y = t^3$

$\dfrac{dx}{dt} = 2t$ $\qquad$ $\dfrac{dy}{dt} = 3t^2$

$$\frac{dy}{dx} = \frac{3t}{2}$$

for $(4,8)$, $\quad t = 2$

$\therefore$ gdt of normal $= -\tfrac{1}{3}$

eqn. of normal, $\dfrac{y-8}{x-4} = -\tfrac{1}{3}$

ie $\quad 3y - 24 = -x + 4$

ie $\quad \underline{x + 3y - 28 = 0}$

at N, $y = 0$ $\quad \therefore x = 28$

Required area $= \displaystyle\int_0^4 x^{3/2}\,dx + \frac{(28-4).8}{2}$

$$= \left[\tfrac{2}{5}x^{5/2}\right]_0^4 + 96$$

$$= \tfrac{2}{5}.32 + 96$$

$$= 12.8 + 96$$

$= \underline{108.8 \text{ sq. units}}$

---

17. Let A be the set of the first five questions
and B " " " " " second " "

3 from A and 4 from B
can be selected in $({}^5C_3) \times ({}^5C_4) = \frac{5!}{2!3!} \times \frac{5!}{1!4!}$

$= 10 \times 5 = \underline{50 \text{ ways}}$

$\therefore$ 4 from A and 3 from B can be selected in :- 50 ways

5 from A and 2 from B
can be selected in $({}^5C_5) \times ({}^5C_2) = \frac{5!}{0!5!} \times \frac{5!}{3!2!}$

$= 1 \times 10 = \underline{10 \text{ ways}}$

The seven questions can be selected in 50+50+10
$= \underline{110 \text{ ways}}$

18.

We require set of values of x for which

$$x > |3x-8|$$

i.e., $x^2 > (3x-8)^2$

i.e., $x^2 > 9x^2 - 48x + 64$

i.e., $0 > 8x^2 - 48x + 64$

i.e., $0 > x^2 - 6x + 8$

i.e., $0 > (x-2)(x-4)$

	+	−
$x-2$	$x>2$	$x<2$
$x-4$	$x>4$	$x<4$

we require "+ −" or "− +"

$\therefore$ $\underline{2 < x < 4}$

June 84 - B2 - 2 and 4

19

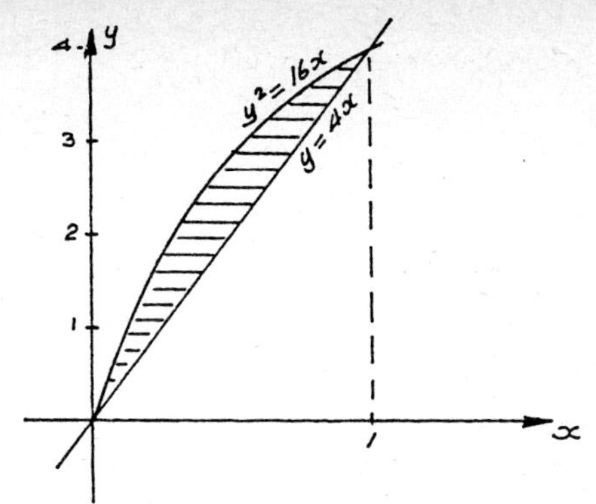

$y^2 = 16x$ and $y = 4x$ intersect at the point where $16x = (4x)^2$

i.e., $16x = 16x^2$

i.e, $x = 0, 1$

Area between $y^2 = 16x$, the co-ordinate axes, and the line $x = 1$

$$= \int_0^1 (16x)^{1/2} dx = \int_0^1 4x^{1/2} dx$$

Area between $y = 4x$, the coordinate axes, and the line $x = 1$

$$= \int_0^1 4x\, dx$$

$\therefore$ Required (shaded) area

$$= \int_0^1 (4x^{1/2} - 4x) dx$$

$$= 4\int_0^1 (x^{1/2} - x) dx$$

$$= 4\left[\tfrac{2}{3}x^{3/2} - \tfrac{x^2}{2}\right]_0^1$$

$$= 4\left\{\left(\tfrac{2}{3} - \tfrac{1}{2}\right) - (0-0)\right\}$$

$$= \tfrac{2}{3}$$, as required

Jan 82 B2 3

20 $\sin x - \cos x \equiv R\sin(x-\alpha)$

$\equiv R\sin x\cos\alpha - R\cos x\sin\alpha$

Equating coefficients :-

$R\cos\alpha = 1$

$R\sin\alpha = 1$

(Right-angled triangle: hypotenuse R, angle α, opposite side $R\sin\alpha = 1$, adjacent side $R\cos\alpha = 1$)

$R = \sqrt{2}$, $\alpha = \tan^{-1}1 = 45°$

$\therefore$ $\underline{\sin x - \cos x \equiv \sqrt{2}\sin(x - 45°)}$ or $\underline{\sqrt{2}\sin(x - \pi/4)}$

$\sin x - \cos x = 1$

can be written $\sqrt{2}\sin(x - 45°) = 1$

$\sin(x - 45°) = 1/\sqrt{2}$

$x - 45° = 45°, 135°, 405°, \ldots$

$x = 90°, 180°, 450°, \ldots$

or $x = \frac{\pi}{2}, \pi, \frac{5\pi}{2}, 3\pi, \ldots$

General Solution :- $\underline{x = \frac{3n\pi}{4} \pm \frac{\pi}{4}}$ $(n = 1, 2, 3, \ldots)$

---

21 $\sum_{r=1}^{n+1} u_r = u_1 + u_2 + u_3 + \ldots$ is a G.P with common ratio k. — ①

$\sum_{r=1}^{n} (u_r u_{r+1}) = u_1u_2 + u_2u_3 + u_3u_4 + \ldots$ — ②

from ① common ratio $k = \frac{u_2}{u_1} = \frac{u_3}{u_2} = \ldots$

from ②, $\frac{\text{2nd term}}{\text{1st term}} = \frac{u_2u_3}{u_1u_2} = k^2$

$\frac{\text{3rd term}}{\text{2nd term}} = \frac{u_3u_4}{u_2u_3} = k^2$

Similarly, $\frac{n\text{th term}}{(n-1)\text{th term}} = k^2$

thus, ② $\underline{\text{is a G.P with first term} = u_1u_2 \text{ and common ratio} = k^2}$

Sum to n terms $=$ "$\frac{a(1-r^n)}{1-r}$", with usual notation

$= \frac{u_1u_2(1-k^{2n})}{(1-k^2)}$

but $u_2 = ku_1$

$\therefore$ $\underline{\text{Sum to } n \text{ terms} = \frac{u_1^2(1-k^{2n})}{1-k^2}}$, as required

---

Jan 83 - B2 4 and 5

22 $\quad f(x) \equiv x^2 - 6x + 10$

$\therefore\ f(x) \equiv (x-3)^2 - 9 + 10$ by "completing square"

$f(x) \equiv (x-3)^2 + 1$

$(x-3)^2 \geqslant 0$ for all real x

$f(x) \geqslant 1$, and hence >0, for all real x

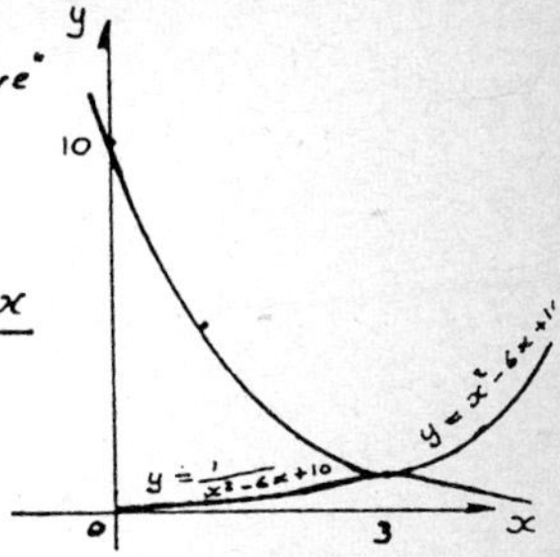

---

23 $\quad f(x) \equiv \dfrac{1}{(x+1)(x+3)}$

Let $\quad \dfrac{A}{x+1} + \dfrac{B}{x+3} \equiv \dfrac{1}{(x+1)(x+3}$

$\therefore\ A(x+3) + B(x+1) \equiv 1$

$x = -3, \quad -2B = 1 \qquad\qquad x = 1, \quad -2A = 1$

$B = -\tfrac{1}{2}. \qquad\qquad A = \tfrac{1}{2}$

$f(x) \equiv \dfrac{1}{2(x+1)} - \dfrac{1}{2(x+3)}$

$$\sum_{r=1}^{r=n} \frac{1}{(2r+1)(2r+3)} \equiv \frac{1}{2(2r+1)} - \frac{1}{2(2r+3)} \equiv \frac{1}{2}\left\{\frac{1}{2r+1} - \frac{1}{2r+3}\right\}$$

if $r=1$, we have $\quad \frac{1}{2}\left\{\frac{1}{3} - \frac{1}{5}\right\}$

$r=2$, " " $\quad \frac{1}{2}\left\{\frac{1}{5} - \frac{1}{7}\right\}$

$\vdots \qquad \vdots \qquad \vdots \qquad\qquad \vdots \qquad \vdots$

$r=n-1$ " " $\quad \frac{1}{2}\left\{\frac{1}{2n-1} - \frac{1}{2n+1}\right\}$

$r=n$ " " $\quad \frac{1}{2}\left\{\frac{1}{2n+1} - \frac{1}{2n+3}\right\}$

Adding the n terms, we have

Sum to n terms $= \frac{1}{2}\left\{\frac{1}{3} - \frac{1}{2n+3}\right\}$

$$= \frac{1}{2}\left\{\frac{2n}{3(2n+3)}\right\} = \frac{n}{3(2n+3)}$$

Jan 83 B2 - 6 and 7

24 Volume of the cylinder $= \pi r^2 h$

$$\therefore \quad \pi r^2 h = 16\pi$$

$$\therefore \quad h = \frac{16}{r^2} \quad \text{—①}$$

Surface Area $= A = 2\pi r h + 2\pi r^2$

$$= 2\pi . \frac{16}{r} + 2\pi r^2$$

When A is a minimum, $\frac{dA}{dr} = 0$

ie, $-\frac{32\pi}{r^2} + 4\pi r = 0$

$$\therefore \quad r^3 = 8$$

$$\therefore \quad \underline{r = 2m}$$

subs. $r = 2$ in ①

$$\underline{h = \frac{16}{4} = 4m.}$$

<u>height = 4m , radius = 2m</u>

---

25 we have $g : x \rightarrow \frac{2x+5}{x-3}$, $x \in \mathbb{R}$, $x \neq 3$

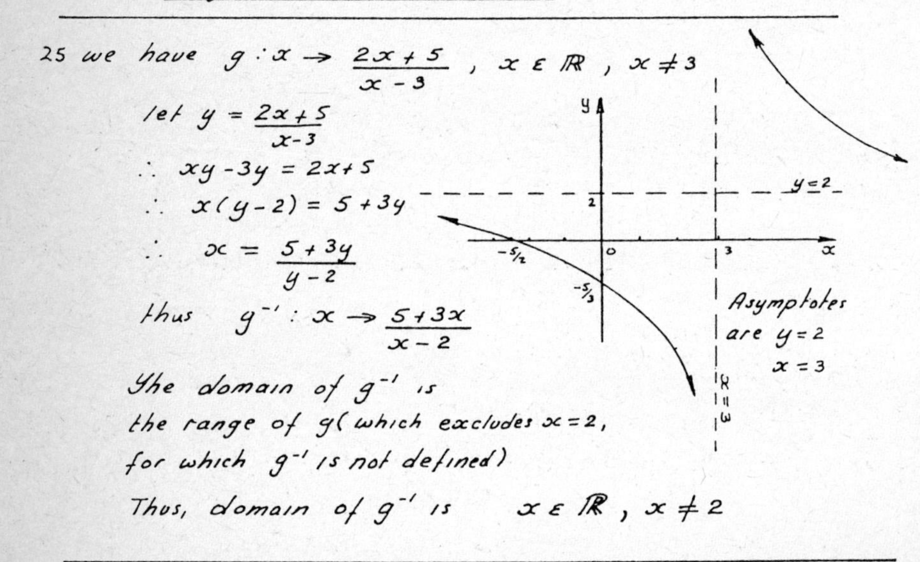

let $y = \frac{2x+5}{x-3}$

$\therefore \quad xy - 3y = 2x + 5$

$\therefore \quad x(y-2) = 5 + 3y$

$\therefore \quad x = \frac{5+3y}{y-2}$

thus $g^{-1} : x \rightarrow \frac{5+3x}{x-2}$

The domain of g^{-1} is the range of g (which excludes $x = 2$, for which g^{-1} is not defined)

Thus, domain of g^{-1} is $x \in \mathbb{R}$, $x \neq 2$

---

26 We have $\bar{r} = \bar{k} + s(\bar{i} + \bar{j})$
$\bar{r} = \bar{k} + t(-\bar{i} + \bar{k})$ } intersecting at A.

from which $s = 0,\ t = 0$ (by putting $\bar{k} + s(\bar{i} + \bar{j}) = \bar{k} + t(-\bar{i} + \bar{k})$)

Thus A has position vector $= \bar{k}$

Consider the plane containing both lines

Let B, C be points where $s = 1$, $t = 1$

$\therefore$ B has position vector $\bar{r}_B = \bar{i} + \bar{j} + \bar{k}$

and C " " " $\bar{r}_C = -\bar{i} + 2\bar{k}$

let $\bar{n} = a\bar{i} + b\bar{j} + c\bar{k}$ be a normal vector to

both $\overline{AB}$ and $\overline{AC}$, where $\overline{AB} = (\bar{i} + \bar{j})$, $\overline{BC} = (-\bar{i} + \bar{k})$

Using Scalar Products :- $(a\bar{i} + b\bar{j} + c\bar{k}) \cdot (\bar{i} + \bar{j}) = 0 \quad \therefore a + b = 0$

$(a\bar{i} + b\bar{j} + c\bar{k}) \cdot (-\bar{i} + \bar{k}) = 0 \quad \therefore -a + c = 0$

from which $a = -b = c$

thus $(a\bar{i} + b\bar{j} + c\bar{j}) = a(\bar{i} - \bar{j} + \bar{k})$

$\therefore$ any scalar multiple of $(\bar{i} - \bar{j} + \bar{k})$ is perpendicular to both lines

The plane can be defined :- $\bar{r} \cdot \bar{n} = \bar{k} \cdot \bar{n}$

ie $\bar{r} \cdot (\bar{i} - \bar{j} + \bar{k}) = \bar{k} \cdot (\bar{i} - \bar{j} + \bar{k})$

ie $\bar{r}(\bar{i} - \bar{j} + \bar{k}) = 1$

---

27 $f(x) = x^3 + 2x + 4$, which is a continuous function.

$\therefore f'(x) = 3x^2 + 2$. Now $3x^2 \geqslant 0$ for all real x

$\therefore f'(x) > 0$ " " " x

Thus $f(x)$ is a continuous increasing function and therefore there is one, and only one, value of x for which $f(x) = 0$

ie, one real root.

We have $f(-2) = -8$ and $f(-1) = 1$

$\therefore f(x) = 0$ in the interval $-2 < x < -1$

Using the given iterative formula with $x_1 = -1$

$$x_2 = -\tfrac{1}{6}(-1^3 - 4(-1) + 4) = -1.166$$

$$x_3 = -\tfrac{1}{6}(-1.166^3 - 4(-1.166) + 4) = -1.179$$

$$= -1.18 \text{ to } 2 \text{ dp.}$$

Jan 83. B2 10 and 11

28 We have $\dfrac{1-kx^2}{(1-x^2)^{1/2}}$ · ie, $(1-kx^2)(1-x^2)^{-1/2}$

Using the binomial expansion :-

$$(1-x^2)^{-1/2} = 1 + (-\tfrac{1}{2})(-x^2) + (-\tfrac{1}{2})(-\tfrac{3}{2})\frac{(-x^2)^2}{2!} + (-\tfrac{1}{2})(-\tfrac{3}{2})(-\tfrac{5}{2})\frac{(-x^2)^3}{3!} + \cdots$$

$$= 1 + \frac{x^2}{2} + \frac{3x^4}{8} + \frac{5x^6}{16} + \cdots$$

multiplying by $(1-kx^2)$

$$\begin{array}{l} 1 - kx^2 \\ \hline 1 + \frac{x^2}{2} + \frac{3x^4}{8} + \frac{5x^6}{16} + \cdots \\ \quad -kx^2 - \frac{kx^4}{2} - \frac{3kx^6}{8} + \cdots \\ \hline 1 + (\tfrac{1}{2}-k)x^2 + (\tfrac{3}{8}-\tfrac{k}{2})x^4 + (\tfrac{5}{16}-\tfrac{3k}{8})x^6 \end{array}$$

coefficient of $x^2 = 0$ $\therefore$ $\underline{k = \tfrac{1}{2}}$

and expansion is $\underline{1 + \dfrac{x^4}{8} + \dfrac{x^6}{8} + \cdots}$

---

29 $$\frac{dy}{dx} = \frac{(y^2-1)}{x}$$

$$\therefore \int \frac{dy}{y^2-1} = \int \frac{dx}{x}$$

$$\therefore \frac{1}{2}\int \left(\frac{1}{y-1} - \frac{1}{y+1}\right) dy = \int \frac{dx}{x}$$

$$\therefore \frac{1}{2}\left(\ln(y-1) - \ln(y+1)\right) = \ln x + \ln A \quad (A = \text{constant})$$

$$\therefore \ln\left(\frac{y-1}{y+1}\right)^{1/2} = \ln(Ax)$$

$$\therefore \left(\frac{y-1}{y+1}\right)^{1/2} = Ax$$

$y = 2,\ x = 1$ $\quad \therefore \left(\frac{1}{3}\right)^{1/2} = A$

$$\therefore \left(\frac{y-1}{y+1}\right)^{1/2} = \frac{1}{\sqrt{3}}\,x$$

from which $\quad 3y - 3 = x^2y + x^2$

$$\therefore (3 - x^2)y = x^2 + 3$$

$$\therefore y = \frac{3 + x^2}{3 - x^2}$$

Jan 83 - B2 - 12 and 13

30. $z_1 = \dfrac{1+i}{1-i}$ $\qquad$ $z_2 = \dfrac{\sqrt{2}}{1-i}$

$\therefore z_1 = \dfrac{(1+i)(1+i)}{(1-i)(1+i)}$ $\qquad$ $\therefore z_2 = \dfrac{\sqrt{2}(1+i)}{(1-i)(1+i)}$

$\therefore z_1 = \dfrac{2i}{2}$ $\qquad$ $\therefore z_2 = \dfrac{\sqrt{2}}{2}(1+i)$

$\therefore z_1 = i$

Modulus of $z_1 = 1$ $\qquad$ Modulus of $z_2 = \frac{\sqrt{2}}{2}(1^2+1^2)^{1/2} = 1$

Argument of $z_1 = \pi/2$ $\qquad$ Argument of $z_2 = \tan^{-1} 1 = \pi/4$

in diagram, $\alpha = \pi/4 / 2 = \pi/8$

thus, the argument of $(z_1 + z_2)$

$= \pi/4 + \alpha = \pi/4 + \pi/8 = 3\pi/8$.

but argument of $(z_1 + z_2) = \tan^{-1} \dfrac{(1 + \sqrt{2}/2)}{\sqrt{2}/2}$

$\therefore \tan 3\pi/8 = \dfrac{1 + \sqrt{2}/2}{\sqrt{2}/2} = \dfrac{2}{\sqrt{2}} + 1$

$= 1 + \sqrt{2}$ (as required)

---

31. $x = at^2$, $y = 2at$

$\dfrac{dx}{dt} = 2at$, $\dfrac{dy}{dt} = 2a$

$\therefore \dfrac{dy}{dx} = \dfrac{dy}{dt} \times \dfrac{dt}{dx} = \dfrac{1}{t}$

thus gradient of tangent at P with parameter $t_1 = 1/t_1$

and gradient of normal at $P = -t_1$.

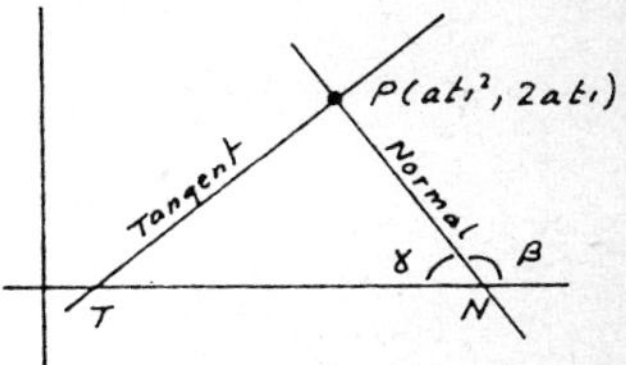

in diagram, $PT/PN = \tan\gamma$

$\tan\gamma = -\tan\beta$

$= +t_1$

the diagram is for the case $t_1 > 0$. If $t_1 < 0$, the diagram would be the reflection of the above in the line $y = 0$ - (the x-axis)

in this case also, $\tan\gamma > 0$

thus $\tan\gamma = -t_1$.

$\therefore$ we have $PT/PN = |t_1|$ (as required)

Jan 83 B2 14 and 15.

32 (a) We require $\frac{1}{3-x} < \frac{1}{x-2}$

ie, $\frac{1}{3-x} - \frac{1}{x-2} < 0$

ie, $\frac{(x-2)-(3-x)}{(3-x)(x-2)} < 0$

ie $\frac{(2x-5)}{(3-x)(x-2)} < 0$

True if the signs are :-

$\frac{(+)}{(+)(-)}$ or $\frac{(+)}{(-)(+)}$ or $\frac{(-)}{(+)(+)}$ or $\frac{(-)}{(-)(-)}$

	+	−
$2x-5$	$x > 5/2$	$x < 5/2$
$3-x$	$x < 3$	$x > 3$
$x-2$	$x > 2$	$x < 2$

referring to the table, we require:-

$x > 5/2$, $x < 3$, $x < 2$:- impossible

$x > 5/2$, $x > 3$, $x > 2$:- $x > 3$

$x < 5/2$, $x < 3$, $x > 2$:- $2 < x < 5/2$

$x < 5/2$, $x > 3$, $x < 2$:- impossible

Thus :- $\frac{1}{3-x} < \frac{1}{x-2}$ if $x > 3$ or $2 < x < 5/2$

(b) we require $|3+2x| \leq |4-x|$

ie, $+\sqrt{(3+2x)^2} \leq +\sqrt{(4-x)^2}$

ie, $(3+2x)^2 \leq (4-x)^2$

ie, $9 + 12x + 4x^2 \leq 16 - 8x + x^2$

ie, $3x^2 + 20x - 7 \leq 0$

ie, $(3x-1)(x+7) \leq 0$

True if signs are :-

$(+,0)(-,0)$ or $(-,0)(+,0)$

	+	−	0
$3x-1$	$x > 1/3$	$x < 1/3$	$x = 1/3$
$x+7$	$x > -7$	$x < -7$	$x = -7$

we require :-

$x \geq 1/3$, $x \leq -7$:- impossible

$x \leq 1/3$, $x \geq -7$:- $-7 \leq x \leq 1/3$

Thus:- $|3+2x| \leq |4-x|$ if $-7 \leq x \leq 1/3$

33 By symmetry, centre of mass, G, lies on X-X axis.
Let base radius of cone $= r$ and mass per unit volume $= m$
Consider a thin disc, δx wide, distance x from Y-Y
By similar triangles, radius of disc :- $y = (h-x)\frac{r}{h}$
mass of disc $= m\pi\left((h-x)\frac{r}{h}\right)^2 \delta x$
and moment of mass about Y-Y $= \frac{mr^2}{h^2}\pi(h-x)^2 x\,\delta x$
Sum of all such moments $= \int_0^h \frac{mr^2}{h^2}\pi(h-x^2)x\,dx$

$$= \frac{mr^2}{h^2}\pi\int_0^h (h^2x - 2hx^2 - x^3)\,dx$$

$$= \frac{mr^2}{h^2}\pi\left[\frac{h^2x^2}{2} - \frac{2hx^3}{3} - \frac{x^4}{4}\right]_0^h$$

$$= \frac{mr^2}{h^2}\pi\left\{\frac{h^4}{2} - \frac{2h^4}{3} - \frac{h^4}{4}\right\}$$

$$= mr^2\pi\frac{h^2}{12}$$

Mass of the cone $= \frac{1}{3}\pi r^2 hm$
Its moment of mass about Y-Y $= \frac{1}{3}\pi r^2 hm\bar{x}$, $\bar{x}$ = distance from Y-Y of G.

We have moment of sum = sum of moments, ie $\frac{1}{3}\pi r^2 hm\bar{x} = mr^2\frac{\pi h^2}{12}$
from which $\bar{x} = h/12$, as required.

Let T = tension in rod
$\cos\theta = \frac{\sqrt{3}h}{2h}$, $\sin\theta = \frac{1}{2}$
Moments abt. A;
$W \times \frac{3h}{4}\sin\theta = Th\cos\theta$
$\therefore W \times \frac{3}{4}\cdot\frac{1}{2} = T\frac{\sqrt{3}}{2}$
$\therefore T = \frac{\sqrt{3}W}{4}$, as required. — ①

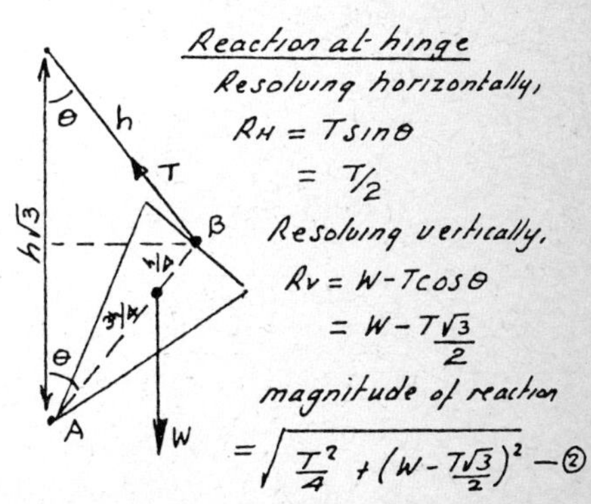

Reaction at hinge
Resolving horizontally,
$R_H = T\sin\theta$
$= T/2$
Resolving vertically,
$R_V = W - T\cos\theta$
$= W - T\frac{\sqrt{3}}{2}$
magnitude of reaction
$= \sqrt{\frac{T^2}{4} + \left(W - \frac{T\sqrt{3}}{2}\right)^2}$ — ②

from ① & ② we have magnitude of reaction at A $= \sqrt{\frac{3W^2}{64} + \frac{25W^2}{64}}$

$$= \frac{\sqrt{7}}{4}W$$

June 82 B3.1

34 Suppose that the spring is extended by an amount y.
Tension $= \lambda y/a$. Let spring be extended a further, infinitesimally small, amount δy. Work done $=$ Tension $\times \delta y = \frac{\lambda y}{a}\delta y$
Total work done stretching spring a distance x

$$= \int_0^x \frac{\lambda y}{a}\,dy = \frac{\lambda}{a}\left[\frac{y^2}{2}\right]_0^x = \frac{\lambda x^2}{2a}$$

$\therefore$ Energy stored in spring (elastic energy) $= \frac{\lambda x^2}{2a}$

As required

Acceleration down plane $= g\sin\frac{\pi}{6}$

$= \frac{g}{2}$

using "$v^2 = u^2 + 2as$";

after distance b $\quad v^2 = g(b+x)$

Kinetic Energy $= \frac{1}{2}mg(b+x)$

When spring has been compressed distance x.

Elastic energy $=$ "$\frac{\lambda x^2}{2a}$" $= \frac{mga}{2ac}x^2$

Loss of KE $= \frac{mgx^2}{2c}$

$\therefore$ Remaining KE $= \frac{1}{2}mg(b+x) - \frac{1}{2}\frac{mgx^2}{c}$

If v = velocity, $\quad \frac{1}{2}mv^2 = \frac{1}{2}mg(b+x) - \frac{1}{2}\frac{mgx^2}{c}$

$$\frac{cv^2}{g} = c(b+x) - x^2$$ As required

if Velocity $= 0$ (for the first time)

$$c(b+x) - x^2 = 0$$

$c = a/10$, $b = 2a$ $\quad \therefore \frac{a}{10}(2a+x) - x^2 = 0$

$\therefore\ 2a^2 + ax - 10x^2 = 0$

$\therefore\ 10x^2 - ax - 2a^2 = 0$

$\therefore\ (5x+2a)(2x-a) = 0$

$\therefore\ x = a/2$, when trolley comes to rest.

Total distance covered $= b + a/2$

$= 2a + \frac{a}{2}$

$= \frac{5a}{2}$

35 We have, acceleration $= -be^{v/u}$

$$\therefore \frac{dv}{dt} = -be^{v/u} \quad \text{———} \quad (1)$$

$$\therefore \int e^{-v/u}\,dv = -\int b\,dt$$

$$\therefore \quad ue^{-v/u} = bt + A \quad (A = \text{constant})$$

when $t = 0$, $v = u$ $\therefore$ $A = \mu e^{-1}$

$$\therefore \quad bt = \mu(e^{-v/u} - e^{-1})$$

$t = t_1$, $v = \tfrac{1}{2}u$ $\therefore$ $bt_1 = \mu(e^{-1/2} - e^{-1})$, as required

time when $v = 0$, $\quad bt = \mu(e^{0} - e^{-1})$

$$\therefore t = \frac{\mu}{b}(1 - e^{-1})$$

Further time $\quad t_2 = \frac{\mu}{b}(1 - e^{-1}) - t_1$

$$= \frac{u}{b}(1 - e^{-1} - e^{-1/2} + e^{-1})$$

$$t_2 = \frac{\mu}{b}(1 - e^{-1/2})$$

$$t_2/t_1 = \frac{\mu}{b}(1 - e^{-1/2}) \Big/ \frac{\mu}{b}(e^{-1/2} - e^{-1})$$

$$= \frac{1 - e^{-1/2}}{e^{-1/2} - e^{-1}} = e^{1/2}, \text{ as required}$$

from (1) $\quad \frac{dv}{dt} = -be^{v/u}$

$$\therefore \frac{dx}{dt}\cdot\frac{dv}{dx} = -be^{v/u}$$

$$\therefore \quad v\frac{dv}{dx} = -be^{v/u}$$

$$\therefore \int ve^{-v/u}\,dv = -b\int dx$$

integrating by parts, $-(v + u)ue^{-v/u} = -bx + B$ $\quad (B = \text{constant})$

if $v = u$, we have $-2u^2e^{-1} = -bx_1 + B$ ——— (3)

if $v = 0$, we have $-\mu^2 = -bx_2 + B$ ——— (4)

(3) − (4) $\quad -2u^2e^{-1} + u^2 = b(x_2 - x_1)$

$$\therefore \quad x_2 - x_1 = \frac{\mu^2}{b}(1 - 2e^{-1})$$

June 82 B3.3

36 We have $\bar{p} = 2a\bar{i} + (a\cos wt)\bar{j} + (a\sin wt)\bar{k}$

$$\bar{q} = (a\sin wt)\bar{i} - (a\cos wt)\bar{j} + 3a\bar{k}$$

Position vector of P relative to Q = $\bar{p} - \bar{q} = \bar{r}$

$$\bar{r} = a(2 - \sin wt)\,\bar{i} + 2a(\cos wt)\,\bar{j} + a(\sin wt - 3)\,\bar{k}$$

we differentiate $\bar{r}$ with respect to t to obtain $\bar{v}$

$$\bar{v} = \frac{d\bar{r}}{dt} = a(-w\cos wt)\bar{i} + 2a(-w\sin wt)\bar{j} + a(w\cos wt)\bar{k}$$

$$\bar{v} = -aw(\cos wt)\bar{i} - 2aw(\sin wt)\bar{j} + aw(\cos wt)\bar{k}$$

For $\bar{r}$ and $\bar{v}$ to be perpendicular, their scalar product = 0

$\therefore\ -a^2w(2 - \sin wt)(\cos wt) - 4a^2w(\cos wt)(\sin wt) + a^2w(\sin wt - 3)(\cos wt) =$

$\therefore\ -2\cos wt + \sin wt\cos wt - 4\sin wt\cos wt + \sin wt\cos wt - 3\cos wt = 0$

$\therefore\ -5\cos wt - 2\sin wt\cos wt = 0$

$\therefore\ \cos wt\,(5 + 2\sin wt) = 0$

$\therefore\ \cos wt = 0 \quad , \quad 2\sin wt = -5$

$\therefore\ wt = \pi/2,\ 3\pi/2,\ \ldots$ and $wt = \sin^{-1} -5/2$

(impossible)

$$\therefore t = \frac{\pi}{2w},\ \frac{3\pi}{2w},\ \ldots$$

$$\therefore t = \frac{(2n-1)\pi}{2w} \quad \text{for } n = 1, 2, 3, 4, \ldots$$

$\bar{r}$ and $\bar{v}$ perpendicular.

$\bar{r}$ = position vector of P relative to Q ie, we have 'stopped' Q and we are considering the motion of P relative to the 'fixed' point Q.

When $\bar{r}$ and $\bar{v}$ are perpendicular, $\bar{v}$ is tangential to $\bar{r}$ and, therefore, $|\bar{r}|$ is a maximum or a minimum.

locus of P

max $|\bar{r}|$

min $|\bar{r}|$

Q

for $t = \pi/2w$

$$\bar{r} = a(2-1)\bar{i} + 2a(0)\bar{j} + a(1-3)\bar{k}$$

$$\bar{r} = a(\bar{i} - 2\bar{k}) \quad \therefore |\bar{r}| = a\sqrt{1+4} = \sqrt{5}\,a$$

for $t = \frac{3\pi}{2w}$

$$\bar{r} = a(2+1)i + 2a(0)\bar{j} + a(-1-3)\bar{k}$$

$$\bar{r} = a(3\bar{i} - 4\bar{k}) \quad \therefore |r| = a\sqrt{9+16} = 5a$$

Smallest and greatest distances between P and Q are, respectively, $\sqrt{5}\,a$ and $5a$

37

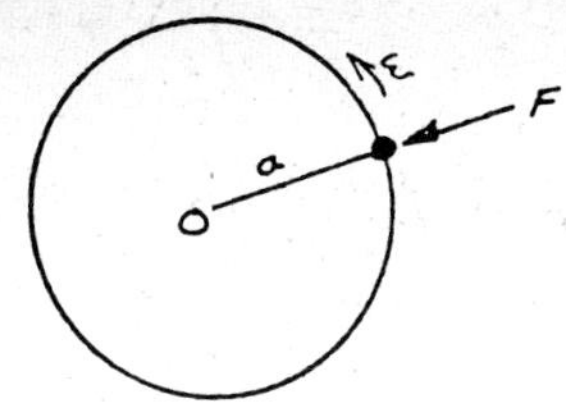

Force to centre $= m\omega^2 r$

where m = mass, ω = angular velocity

r = radius of orbit.

$$\therefore F = m\omega^2 a$$

$$\therefore \omega = \sqrt{\frac{F}{ma}}$$

Period of satellite $= \dfrac{2\pi}{\omega}$

$$\therefore T = 2\pi\sqrt{\frac{ma}{F}}$$

if gravitational force $= m\mu/r^2$, where r = radius of path

then $T^2 = 4\pi^2 \dfrac{ma}{m\mu/a^2} = \dfrac{4\pi^2 a^3}{\mu}$

$\therefore \mu T^2 = 4\pi^2 a^3$ – as required

Gravitational force, on earth's surface, $= 10m$

$$\therefore 10m = \frac{m\mu^2}{(6400 \times 1000)^2}$$

from which, $\mu = (6.4)^2 \times 10^{13}$, as required

radius of path $= (6400 + 600) = 7000$ km

using $\mu T^2 = 4\pi^2 a^3$, we have :-

$$T^2 \times (6.4)^2 \times 10^{13} = 4\pi^2 \times (7000 \times 1000)^3$$

$$\therefore T = \frac{\sqrt{\dfrac{4\pi^2 \times (7000 \times 1000)^3}{(6.4)^2 \times 10^{13}}}}{60 \times 60} \text{ hours.}$$

$$= \underline{1.60 \text{ hours}}$$

June 82. B3. 5

38. Let u_A, u_B = velocities of A, B before impact

and v_A, v_B = " " A, B after "

$\therefore u_A = v$, $u_B = 0$, $v_A = ?$, $v_B = 3u$

also, mass of A = m, mass of B = $3m$, $e = \frac{1}{2}$

Newton :- $v_A - v_B = -e(u_A - u_B)$

$\therefore v_A - 3u = -\frac{1}{2}(v - 0)$

$\therefore v_A = 3u + \frac{v}{2}$ —— ①

Momentum :- $m u_A + 3m u_B = m v_A + 3m v_B$

$\therefore mv = m v_A + 9mu$

$\therefore v = v_A + 9u$ —— ②

From ① and ②

$v = 3u + \frac{v}{2} + 9u$

$\therefore \frac{v}{2} = 12u$

$\therefore$ $\underline{v = 24u}$

$v_A = 3u + 12u$

$\therefore$ $\underline{v_A = 15u}$

= speed of A after impact

(a) Impulse received by B

= change of momentum $= 3m \times v_B = 3m \times 3u = 9mu$

$\therefore$ Impulse $= 9mu$

(b) KE Gained by B = "$\frac{1}{2} mv^2$" $= \frac{1}{2} \times 3m \times 9u^2 = \frac{27}{2} mu^2$

KE Lost by A $= \left(\frac{1}{2} \times m \times 24^2 u^2\right) - \left(\frac{1}{2} \times m \times 15^2 u^2\right) = \frac{351}{2} mu^2$

KE Lost in impact $= \frac{351}{2} mu^2 - \frac{27}{2} mu^2 = 162\, mu^2$

When B strikes C, change of momentum $= 9mu$

$\therefore$ initial velocity of C $= \frac{9mu}{\text{mass of } C} = \frac{9mu}{6m} = \frac{3u}{2}$

initial K.E of C $= \frac{1}{2} \times 6m \times \left(\frac{3u}{2}\right)^2 = \frac{27}{4} mu^2$

Strain energy of C when it comes to rest = "$\frac{1}{2} \frac{\lambda x^2}{l}$"

$= \frac{1}{2} \times \frac{kmg}{l} \times \frac{l^2}{16}$

$= \frac{kmgl}{32}$

$\therefore \frac{kmgl}{32} = \frac{27mu^2}{4}$

$\therefore k = \frac{216u^2}{gl}$, as required

39 Using usual notation.

For vertical motion

u_y = initial velocity = $u \sin\alpha$

acceleration = $-g = -\frac{u^2}{c}$

v_y = velocity at time t

y = height at time t

max height $= h$

$\therefore$ for $y = h$, $v_y = 0$

using "$v^2 = u^2 + 2as$"

$u^2 \sin^2\alpha = \frac{2u^2 h}{c}$

$\therefore \sin^2\alpha = 2h/c$

$\therefore$ $2h = c\sin^2\alpha$, as required — (1)

time of flight

$y = 0$

using "$s = ut + \frac{1}{2}at^2$"

$0 = ut\sin\alpha - \frac{u^2 t^2}{2c}$

$\therefore t = 0, \frac{2c\sin\alpha}{u}$ — (2)

For horizontal motion

u_x = constant velocity = $u\cos\alpha$

from (2) time of flight $= \frac{2c\sin\alpha}{u}$

Range, $R = 2c\sin\alpha\cos\alpha$, as required — (3)

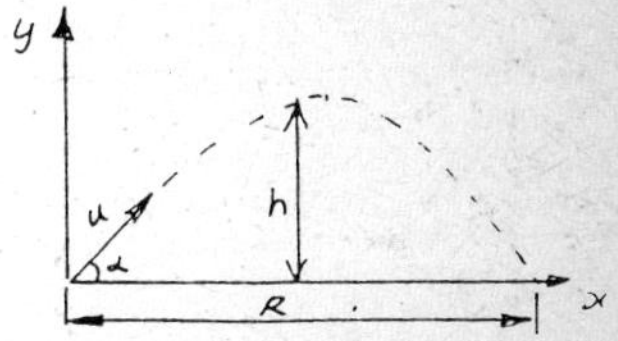

from (3) $R^2 = 4c^2\sin^2\alpha\cos^2\alpha$

$R^2 = 4c^2(\sin^2\alpha)(1-\sin^2\alpha)$ — (4)

from (1) and (4), $R^2 = 4c^2(2h/c)(1 - 2h/c)$

from which $R^2 = 8h(c-2h)$

$\therefore$ $R^2 = c^2 - (c-4h)^2$ as required

We have, $R^2 = c^2 - (c-4h)^2$ with R and h variable

differentiating, $2R\frac{dR}{dh} = -2(c-4h)(-4)$

ie $\frac{dR}{dh} = \frac{16}{R}(c/4 - h)$

For $h < c/4$, $\frac{16}{R}(c/4 - h) > 0$, thus $\frac{dR}{dh} > 0$ and function is increasing

From $R^2 = c^2 - (c-4h)^2$

Greatest range, $R_{MAX} = \sqrt{c^2 - (c-4h)^2}$

for $c = \frac{u^2}{g}$. $R_{MAX} = \sqrt{\frac{u^4}{g^2} - \left(\frac{u^2}{g} - 4h\right)^2}$

We have $u = 30$ m

$h = 20$ m

$R_{MAX} = \sqrt{\frac{30^4}{10^2} - \left(\frac{30^2}{10} - 4.20\right)^2}$

$= 89.4$ m, as required

June 82 . B3. 7.

40

(i) $P(A) = 0.4$, $P(B) = 0.45$, $P(A \cup B) = 0.68$

If mutually exclusive, $P(A \cup B) = P(A) + P(B)$

$= 0.4 + 0.45$

$= 0.85$

$0.85 \neq 0.68$ $\therefore$ A, B not mutually exclusive

$P(A \cap B) = P(A) + P(B) - P(A \cup B) = 0.4 + 0.45 - 0.68 = 0.27$

If independent, $P(A \cap B) = P(A) \times P(B)$

$P(A) \times P(B) = 0.4 \times 0.45 \neq 0.27$

$\therefore$ A, B not independent

(ii) 12 R, 8 B, 4 W balls.

3 balls are selected, without replacement

(a) Same colour :-

$P(R, R, R) = \frac{12}{24} \times \frac{11}{23} \times \frac{10}{22} = \frac{55}{506}$

$P(B, B, B) = \frac{8}{24} \times \frac{7}{23} \times \frac{6}{22} = \frac{14}{506}$

$P(W, W, W) = \frac{4}{24} \times \frac{3}{23} \times \frac{2}{22} = \frac{1}{506}$

$\therefore$ P(all balls are same colour) $= \frac{55 + 14 + 1}{506}$

$= \frac{35}{253}$

(b) Each different

$P(R, B, W) = \frac{12}{24} \times \frac{8}{23} \times \frac{4}{22} = \frac{8}{253}$

R, B, W can be arranged in 3! different ways, each equally likely

$\therefore$ p(each ball different colour $= \frac{3! \times 8}{253}$

$= \frac{48}{253}$

June 82. B3. 8

41 We have Δ PQR with altitude $PS = h$.

For Δ PQS

MN is the line through the centre of mass parallel to, and distance $\bar{x}$, from QR. Let $QS = a$

Consider a thin strip δx wide parallel to, and distance x from, QR.

By similar Δ's, height of strip is $\dfrac{a(h-x)}{h}$.

Area of the strip is $\dfrac{a(h-x)\delta x}{h}$

Mass of strip $= \dfrac{ma(h-x)\delta x}{h}$

(where m = mass / unit area)

Moment of mass (for strip), about QS, $= \dfrac{ma(h-x)x\delta x}{h}$

$$\text{Sum of all moments} = \int_0^h \frac{ma(h-x)x\,dx}{h}$$

$$= \frac{ma}{h}\left[\frac{hx^2}{2} - \frac{x^3}{3}\right]_0^h$$

$$= \frac{mah^2}{6} \quad \text{———— (1)}$$

Mass of Δ PQS $= \frac{1}{2} mah$

Moment of mass, about QS, $= \frac{1}{2} mah\bar{x}$ ———— (2)

From (1) and (2) we have $\frac{1}{2} mah\bar{x} = \dfrac{mah^2}{6}$

$$\therefore \quad \bar{x} = \frac{h}{3}$$

Similarly, the centre of mass of Δ PRS, from QS $= \frac{h}{3}$

Thus:- Centre of mass of Δ PQR, from QS, $= h/3$

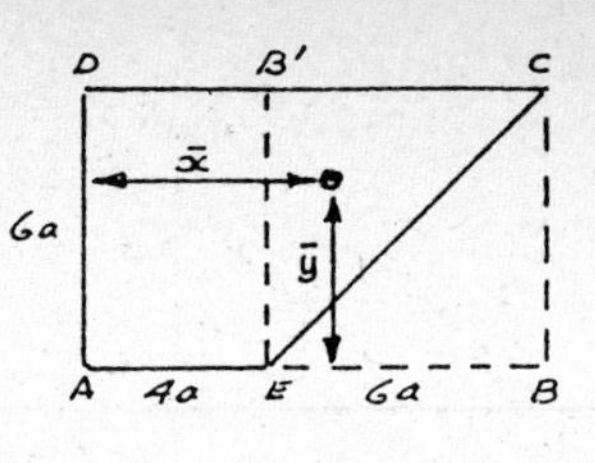

Let distance of centre of mass be $\bar{x}$ from AD and $\bar{y}$ from AE

let m = mass/unit area

Mass AEB'D $= 6a \times 4a \times m = 24a^2m$

Mass EB'C $= 2 \times \frac{1}{2} \times 6a \times 6a = 36a^2m$

Total mass $= 60a^2m$.

$$60a^2m\bar{x} = (24a^2m \times 2a) + (36a^2m \times 6a)$$

$$\bar{x} = \frac{48a + 216a}{60}$$

(a) $\bar{x} = 4{\cdot}4a$

$$60a^2m\bar{y} = (24a^2m \times 3a) + (36a^2m \times 4a)$$

$$\bar{y} = \frac{72a + 144a}{60}$$

(b) $\bar{y} = 3{\cdot}6a$

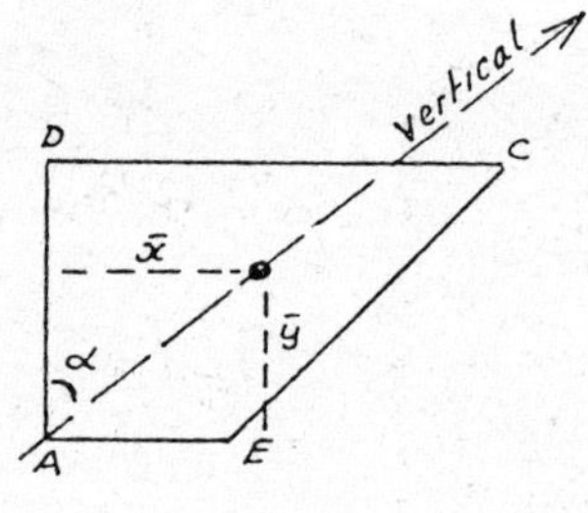

Let α = angle AD makes with the vertical.

$$\tan\alpha = \frac{\bar{x}}{\bar{y}} = \frac{4{\cdot}4}{3{\cdot}6}$$

$$\alpha = \tan^{-1}\frac{11}{9}$$

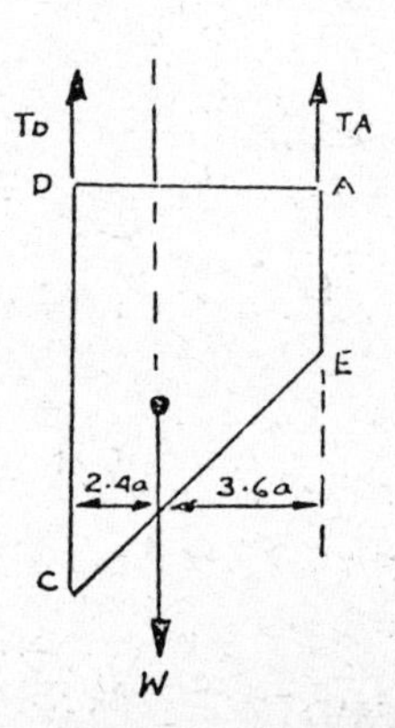

Let T_A, T_D = Tensions in strings

Moments about D :- $W \times 2{\cdot}4a = T_A \times 6a$

$\therefore$ $T_A = 0{\cdot}4W$

Moments about A :- $W \times 3{\cdot}6a = T_D \times 6a$

$T_D = 0{\cdot}6W$

42

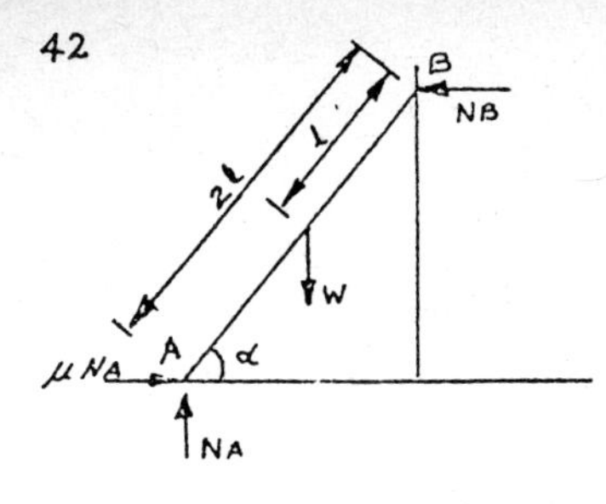

The Forces acting are :-
Weight :- W, Normal Reactions N_A & N_B and, at point of slip, Friction Force $= \mu N_A$.

Resolving Vertically :-

$$N_A = W \quad (1)$$

Resolving Horizontally :-

$$\mu N_A = N_B \quad (2)$$

Moments about A :-

$$W l \cos\alpha = N_B . 2l \sin\alpha$$

$$\therefore W = N_B . 2 \tan\alpha$$

$$\therefore W = 4 N_B \quad (3)$$

from (1) and (2) $\mu W = N_B \quad (4)$

from (3) and (4) $\mu . 4 N_B = N_B$

$$\mu = 1/4$$

this is least value.

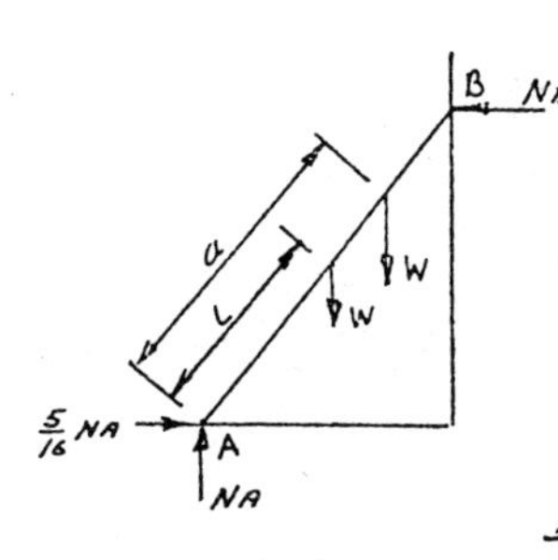

with additional weight W and $\mu = 5/16$

Again, consider AB in equilibrium, and about to slip

let a = distance from A of highest point at which weight W can be placed

Resolving Vertically :-

$$N_A = 2W \quad (5)$$

Resolving Horizontally :-

$$5/16 \; N_A = N_B \quad (6)$$

Moments about A :-

$$W l \cos\alpha + W a \cos\alpha = N_B . 2l \sin\alpha$$

$$W(l + a) = 4 N_B l \quad (7)$$

from (5) and (6) $5/8 \; W = N_B \quad (8)$

from (7) and (8) $W(l + a) = 5/2 \; W l$

$$\therefore a = 5/2 \; l - l$$

$$\therefore a = 3/2 \; l$$

Jan 83. B3. 2.

43

(i)

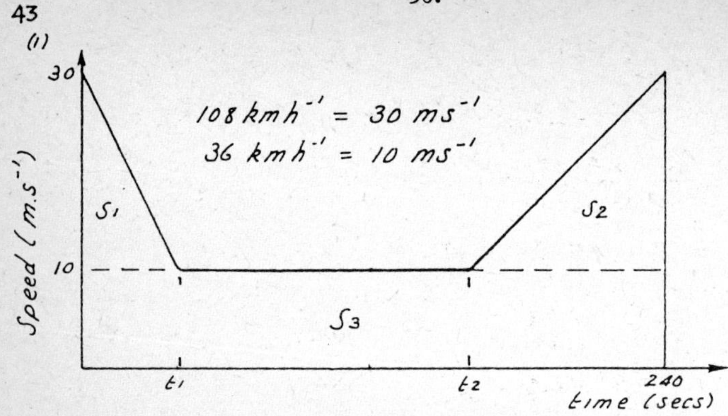

t_1, t_2, S_1, S_2, S_3 are times and distances as indicated in diagram

$S_3 = 10 \times 240 = 2400\,m.$

$S_1 + S_2 + S_3 = 4000\,m.$

$S_1 + S_3 = 4000 - 2400 = 1600\,m.$

Retardation $= 3f$, acceleration $= f$

$\therefore\; S_2 = 3\,S_1$ and $(240 - t_2) = 3t_1.$ — ①

$\therefore\; S_1 = 400\,m \quad S_2 = 1200\,m.$

<u>for S_1 Triangle</u>;

$\frac{1}{2} \times (30-10)\,t_1 = 400$

$t_1 = 40\,secs$

$3f = \frac{(30-10)}{t_1} = \frac{20}{40}$

$\therefore\; \underline{f = \frac{1}{6}\; ms^{-2}}$ <u>(answer (a))</u>

from ① $(240 - t_2) = 3 \times 40$

$t_2 = 120\,secs$

time of constant speed $= (t_2 - t_1) = (120 - 40) = 80\,secs$

<u>Distance travelled at $36\; kmh^{-1} = 10 \times 80 = 800\,m$</u>

<u>answer (b)</u>

(ii) acceleration $= \frac{k}{1+v}$ ms^{-1}

ie. $\frac{dv}{dt} = \frac{k}{1+v}$

now $\frac{dv}{dt} = \frac{dv}{ds} \times \frac{ds}{dt}$

ie. $\frac{dv}{dt} = \frac{dv}{ds} \times v$

$\therefore \quad v\frac{dv}{ds} = \frac{k}{1+v}$

$\int v(1+v)\,dv = \int k\,ds.$

$\frac{v^2}{2} + \frac{v^3}{3} = ks + A$

$3v^2 + 2v^3 = 6ks + B \qquad (B = 6A)$

$v = 0, \qquad 0 = 6kS_0 + B$ — ①

$v = u, \quad 3u^2 + 2u^3 = 6kS_1 + B$ — ②

② − ① $\quad 3u^2 + 2u^3 = 6k(S_1 - S_0)$

Distance travelled $= (S_1 - S_0)$

$= \frac{3u^2 + 2u^3}{6k}$ Answer

---

44 (a) Velocity vector of A $= \bar{v}_A = \dfrac{17(8\bar{i}+15\bar{j})}{\sqrt{8^2+15^2}} = \underline{(8\bar{i}+15\bar{j})}$

" " " B $= \bar{v}_B = \dfrac{15(3\bar{i}+4\bar{j})}{\sqrt{3^2+4^2}} = \underline{(9\bar{i}+12\bar{j})}$

(b) Velocity of B relative to A $= {}_A\bar{v}_B$

${}_A\bar{v}_B = \bar{v}_B - \bar{v}_A = (9\bar{i}+12\bar{j}) - (8\bar{i}+15\bar{j})$

$= (\bar{i} - 3\bar{j})$

ie ${}_Av_B = \sqrt{1^2+3^2} = \underline{\sqrt{10}\text{ knots}}$ <u>in the direction of vector $(\bar{i} - 3\bar{j})$</u>

(C) Position vector of B relative to A at time t hours is $\underline{\bar{r} = 10\bar{j} + (\bar{i} - 3\bar{j})t\text{ miles}}$

Using result of part (c),

at time t, distance r between A and B :-

$r = \sqrt{(t)^2 + (10-3t)^2}$

$r = \sqrt{10t^2 - 60t + 100}$

We require the two times when r = 5 miles

ie $5 = \sqrt{10t^2 - 60t + 100}$

ie $25 = 10t^2 - 60t + 100$

ie $0 = 10t^2 - 60t + 75$

ie $0 = 2t^2 - 12t + 15$

Solving for t we have the two values of t :-

$t_1 = \dfrac{12+\sqrt{24}}{4}$ $\qquad t_2 = \dfrac{12-\sqrt{24}}{4}$

the time for which A & B are within 5 miles is :-

$t_1 - t_2 = \dfrac{2\sqrt{24}}{4} = \sqrt{6}$ hours, as required

45

(i)

$\tan\alpha = 3/4$

$\therefore \sin\alpha = 3/5$; $\cos\alpha = 4/5$

let u = initial velocity of ball, with direction $\tan^{-1} 3/4$.
with usual notation, we have :-

Horizontal motion

$u_x = u \times 4/5 = 4u/5 \ ms^{-1}$

$a = 0.$

t_1 (secs) = time to travel 32m

"$s = ut$"

$32 = 4u/5 \ t_1$

$t_1 = 40/u$ —— ①

Vertical motion

$u_y = u \times 3/5 = 3u/5 \ ms^{-1}$

$a = -10 \ ms^{-2}$

t_1 (secs) = time at which ball has height = 4m

v_y = velocity at time t_1

"$s = ut + 1/2 at^2$"

$4 = 3ut_1/5 - 1/2 . 10 t_1^2$

$20 = 3ut_1 - 25t_1^2$ —— ②

from ① & ② we have :-

$$20 = 3.40 - \frac{25.40^2}{u^2}$$

$$u^2 = 6u^2 - 2000$$

$$\therefore 5u^2 = 2000$$

$$u = 20$$

$\therefore$ initial speed of ball $= 20 \ ms^{-1}$, as required

from ①, $t_1 = 40/20 = 2$ secs.

horizontal component of velocity $= \frac{4 . 20}{5} = 16 \ ms^{-1}$

using "$v = u + at$", vertical component of velocity at $t_1 = 2$ is $\frac{3 . 20}{5} - 10.2$

ie, $-8 \ ms^{-1}$

Speed of ball when it hits goal post

$= \sqrt{8^2 + 16^2} = 8\sqrt{5} \ ms^{-1}$ Answer

Jan 83 B3.'5

46

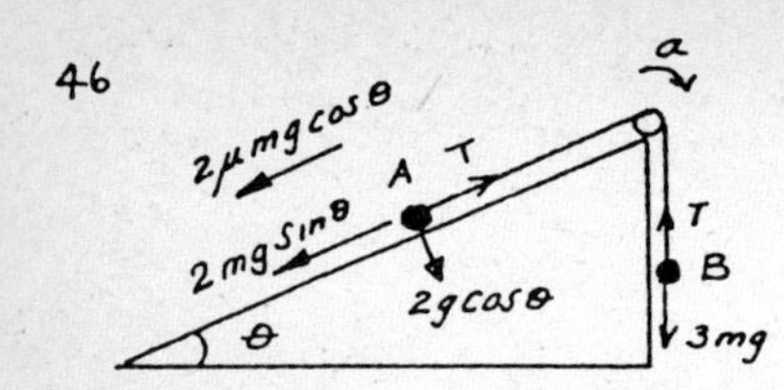

$\tan\theta = 3/4$

$\sin\theta = 3/5$

$\cos\theta = 4/5$

let tension in string = T Newtons

Common acceleration of particles = $a\ ms^{-2}$ (in direction shown)

<u>Consider particle A :- 2m mass</u>

Acc force up plane = $T - 2mg\sin\theta - 2\mu mg\cos\theta$

ie, $2ma = T - 2mg.\frac{3}{5} - 2\mu mg.4/5$

$2ma = T - \frac{6mg}{5} - \frac{8}{5}\mu mg$

$2ma = T - \frac{mg}{5}(6 + 8\mu)$ ——— ①

<u>Consider particle B - 3m mass</u>

Acc force down = $3mg - T$

ie, $3ma = 3mg - T$ ——— ②

(a) <u>Plane smooth</u>

from ① & ② with $\mu = 0$:-

$2ma = T - \frac{6mg}{5}$ — ③

$3ma = -T + 3mg$ — ④

③ + ④ $5ma = \frac{9}{5}mg$

$a = \frac{9}{25}g$

<u>acceleration</u> = $\frac{9}{25}g$ <u>ms^{-2}</u>

subs. in ③

$\frac{2m.9g}{25} = T - \frac{6mg}{5}$

$\therefore T = \frac{48mg}{25}$

<u>Tension</u> = $\frac{48mg}{25}$ <u>NEWTONS</u>

(b) <u>Plane, $\mu = 1/4$</u>

from ① & ② with $\mu = 1/4$

$2ma = T - \frac{8mg}{5}$ — ⑤

$3ma = -T + 3mg$ — ⑥

⑤ + ⑥ $5ma = \frac{7mg}{5}$

$a = \frac{7}{25}g$

<u>acceleration</u> = $\frac{7g}{25}$ <u>ms^{-2}</u>

subs in ⑤

$\frac{14mg}{25} = T - \frac{8}{5}mg$

$T = \frac{54mg}{25}$

<u>Tension</u> = $\frac{54}{25}.mg$ <u>Newtons</u>

Jan 83 B3 6

47 (i)

A: $\mu_A = 2u$, $V_A = ?$, mass $= 3m$ →

B: $u_B = -u$, $V_B = ?$, mass $= m$ →

$e = 1/3$

Let μ_A, μ_B = speeds of A, B before impact
V_A, V_B = " " A, B after "
as shown above.

Newton's Law :- $V_B - V_A = -e(u_B - u_A)$

$\therefore V_B - V_A = -\frac{1}{3}(-u - 2u)$

$\therefore V_B - V_A = u$ — ①

Conservation of momentum :- $3mV_A + mV_B = 3mU_A + mU_B$

$\therefore 3V_A + V_B = 6u - u$

$\therefore V_B + 3V_A = 5u$ — ②

② − ① $4V_A = 4u$

$\therefore V_A = u$

subs in ①, $V_B - u = u$

$V_B = 2u$

Speed of mass m is u and of mass 3m is 2u.

Impulse = change of momentum = $3mu$

(ii) In 1 second

work done by pump = 41000 joules

work done against gravity = "mgh" = $80 \times 10 \times 20$

= 16 000 joules

work done in providing K.E = "$\frac{1}{2}mv^2$"

$= \frac{1}{2} \times 80 \times v^2$

$= 40v^2$

we have $40v^2 = 41000 - 16000$

$\therefore v^2 = 25000/40$

$\therefore v = 50/2$

$\therefore v = 25\,ms^{-1}$

48. (i) Prob. of A occurring $= P(A) = 1/3$

Prob of A not occurring $= P(A') = 2/3$

Prob of B occurring $= P(B) = 1/4$

Prob of B not occurring $= P(B') = 3/4$

(a) $P(A' \text{ and } B') = P(A') \times P(B') = 2/3 \times 3/4 = \frac{1}{2}$

$\therefore$ prob. of neither $= 1/2$

(b) $P(A \text{ and } B') = P(A) \times P(B') = 1/3 \times 3/4 = \frac{3}{12}$

$P(A' \text{ and } B) = P(A') \times P(B) = 2/3 \times 1/4 = \frac{2}{12}$

$\therefore$ P(one - and only one - occurring) $= \frac{3}{12} + \frac{2}{12} = \frac{5}{12}$

(ii) There are :- {R, R, R, B, B, B, W, W, W, W.}

(a) Consider the 2 balls to have same colour :-

$P(R,R) = \frac{3}{10} \times \frac{2}{9} = \frac{6}{90}$

$P(B,B) = \frac{6}{90}$

$P(W,W) = \frac{4}{10} \times \frac{3}{9} = \frac{12}{90}$

P(first 2 balls are same) $= \frac{6}{90} + \frac{6}{90} + \frac{12}{90} = \frac{24}{90} = \frac{4}{15}$

$\therefore$ P(first 2 balls different) $= 1 - 4/15 = 11/15$

(b) $P(R,R,R) = \frac{3}{10} \times \frac{2}{9} \times \frac{1}{8} = \frac{6}{720}$

$P(B,B,B) = \frac{6}{720}$

$P(W,W,W) = \frac{4}{10} \times \frac{3}{9} \times \frac{2}{8} = \frac{24}{720}$

P(3 balls same) $= \frac{6}{720} + \frac{6}{720} + \frac{24}{720} = \frac{1}{20}$

(c) $P\{R,R,R' \text{ (any order)}\} = \frac{3}{10} \times \frac{2}{9} \times \frac{7}{8} \times 3 = \frac{126}{720}$

$P\{B,B,B' \text{ (any order)}\} = \frac{126}{720}$

$P\{W,W,W' \text{ (any order)}\} = \frac{4}{10} \times \frac{3}{9} \times \frac{6}{8} \times 3 = \frac{216}{720}$

$\therefore$ P(exactly 2 balls have same colour)

$= \frac{126}{720} + \frac{126}{720} + \frac{216}{720} = \frac{558}{720} = \frac{31}{40}$

June 84 - B3 - 8

49 (i) Vector equation :- $\bar{r} = 6\bar{i} + 3\bar{j} + 6(\bar{i}\cos\theta + \bar{j}\sin\theta)$

Centre of circle $\doteq$ (6, 3)

radius = 6.

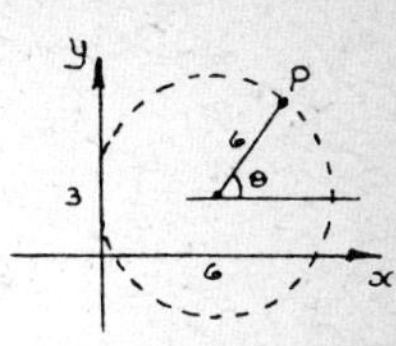

we are given that at $t = 0$, $\theta = 0$

$\therefore$ at time t, $\theta = \omega t = \frac{\pi t}{12}$

thus position vector of P :-

$$\bar{p} = 6\bar{i} + 3\bar{j} + 6(\bar{i}\cos\frac{\pi t}{12} + \bar{j}\sin\frac{\pi t}{12})$$

(ii)

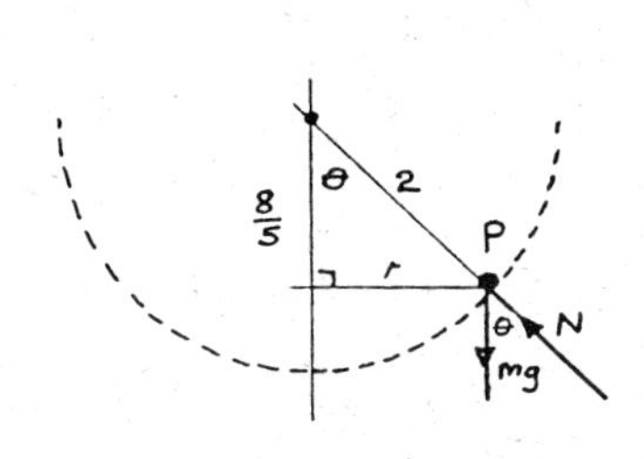

By considering the right angled triangle, $r = 6/5$

The two components of N, the Normal Reaction, are :-

Vertically, $N\cos\theta = mg$ — ①

Horizontally, $N\sin\theta = \frac{mv^2}{r}$ — ②

(where v = speed of the particle)

② ÷ ① :- $\tan\theta = \frac{v^2}{rg}$

$\therefore \frac{6}{5} \times \frac{5}{8} = \frac{v^2}{10} \times \frac{5}{6}$

from which $v^2 = 9$

ie, $v = 3$ m/s (as required)

---

50 Max Power $= S$ kW $= 1000S$ Watts

Let Resistance $= R$ Newtons

<u>on level (with max speed $= u\ ms^{-1}$)</u>

Driving Force $= \frac{\text{Power}}{\text{Velocity}} = \frac{1000S}{u}$ N.

The only force opposing this force $= R$. (at max. speed)

$\therefore R = \frac{1000S}{u}$ N. ——— ①

<u>Slope ($\sin\alpha = 1/16$, max speed $= u/2\ ms^{-1}$)</u>

Driving force $= \frac{2S}{u} \times 1000 = \frac{2000S}{u}$

The two forces opposing motion (at max speed) are :-

$R + mg\sin\alpha$ (where m = mass of car, (kg) and $mg\sin\alpha$ = gravitational force)

$\therefore \frac{2000S}{u} = R + \frac{10m}{16}$

$\therefore \frac{2000S}{u} = \frac{1000S}{u} + \frac{5m}{8}$ (using $R = \frac{1000S}{u}$ from ①)

$\therefore m = \frac{8000S}{5u}$ ——— ②

<u>Slope ($\sin\beta = 1/8$, max speed $= V$, say)</u>

Driving force $= \frac{1000S}{V}$.

Using similar argument to above, $\frac{1000S}{V} = \frac{1000S}{u} + \frac{5m}{4}$

but, from ②, $m = \frac{8000S}{5u}$ $\therefore \frac{1000S}{V} = \frac{1000S}{u} + \frac{2000S}{u}$

$\therefore \frac{1}{V} = \frac{3}{u}$

$\therefore V = u/3$

<u>$\therefore$ max speed up slope ($\sin\beta = 1/8$) is $\frac{u}{3}\ ms^{-1}$</u>

<u>on level with trailer</u> ($S = 15$, $u = 20$)

from ① $R = \frac{1000 \times 15}{20} = 750$N. from ② $m = \frac{8000 \times 15}{5 \times 20}$

$= 1200$ kg

Total mass (car + trailer) $= 1200 + 300 = 1500$ kg

At speed $= 10\ ms^{-1}$ Force $= \frac{1000S}{10} = 1500$N.

Driving force = accelerating force + R

$1500 = ma + 750$

$1500 = 1500a + 750$

$0.5 = a$

<u>Acceleration $= 0.5\ ms^{-2}$</u>

THE BASIC CONCEPTS SERIES

The Basic Concepts series attempts to explain in a clear and concise manner the main concepts involved in a subject. Paragraphs are numbered for ease of reference and key points are emboldened for clear identification, with self assessment questions at the end of each chapter. The texts should prove useful to students studying for A level, professional and first year degree courses. Other titles in the series include:—

Basic Concepts in Business by Tony Hines
Basic Concepts in Foundation Accounting by Tony Hines
Basic Concepts in Financial Mathematics and Statistics
by T.M. Jackson
Basic Concepts in Business Taxation by K. Astbury

QUESTIONS AND ANSWERS SERIES

These highly successful revision aids contain questions and answers based on actual examination questions and provide fully worked answers for each question. The books are written by experienced lecturers and examiners and will be useful for students preparing for O and A level, foundation and BTEC examinations. Subjects include:—

- Economics by G. Walker
- Accounting by T. Hines
- Multiple Choice Economics by Dr. S. Kermally
- O level Mathematics by R.H. Evans
- A level Pure Mathematics and Statistics by R.H. Evans
- A level Pure and Applied Mathematics by R.H. Evans
- O level Physics by R.H. Evans
- O level Chemistry by J. Sheen
- O level Human Biology by D. Reese

NOTES